CATHOLIC CHURCHMEN
IN SCIENCE

Catholic Churchmen in Science

First Series

SKETCHES OF THE LIVES OF CATHOLIC
ECCLESIASTICS WHO WERE AMONG
THE GREAT FOUNDERS IN SCIENCE

BY

JAMES J. WALSH, M.D., Ph.D., LL.D.

Essay Index Reprint Series

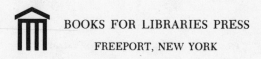

BOOKS FOR LIBRARIES PRESS
FREEPORT, NEW YORK

First published 1906
Reprinted 1968

LIBRARY OF CONGRESS CATALOG CARD NUMBER:

68-16985

PRINTED IN THE UNITED STATES OF AMERICA

"A sorrow's crown of sorrow."

THIS BOOK IS AFFECTIONATELY DEDICATED TO THE
MEMORY OF MY MOTHER.

PREFACE.

THE following sketches of the lives of clergymen who were great scientists have appeared at various times during the past five years in Catholic magazines. They were written because the materials for them had gradually accumulated during the preparation of various courses of lectures, and it seemed advisable to put them in order in such a way that they might be helpful to others working along similar lines. They all range themselves naturally around the central idea that the submission of the human reason to Christian belief, and of the mind and heart to the authority of the qhurch, is quite compatible with original thinking of the highest order, and with that absolute freedom of investigation into physical science, which has only too often been said to be quite impossible to churchmen. For this reason friends have suggested that they should be published together in a form in which they would be more easy of consultation than when scattered in different periodicals. It was urged, too, that they would thus also be more effective for the cause which they uphold. This friendly suggestion has been yielded to, whether justifiably or not the reader must decide for himself. There is so great a flood of books, good, bad, and indifferent, ascribing their existence to the advice of well-meaning friends, that we poor authors are evidently not in a position to judge for ourselves of the merit of our works or of the possible interest they may arouse.

I have to thank the editors of the "American Catholic Quarterly Review," of the "Ave Maria," and of "The Ecclesiastical Review" and "The Dolphin," for their kind permission to republish the articles which appeared originally in their pages. All of them, though substantially remaining the same, have been revised, modified in a number of particulars, and added to very considerably in most cases.

CONTENTS.

(ix)

I.

THE SUPPOSED OPPOSITION OF SCIENCE AND RELIGION.

I.

THE SUPPOSED OPPOSITION OF SCIENCE AND RELIGION.

IT used to be very common to hear it said and to read that there was serious opposition between science and religion. This persuasion has been minimized to a great degree in recent years, and yet sufficient of it remains to make a great many people think that, if there is not entire incompatibility between science and religion, there is at least such a diversity of purposes and aims in these two great realms of human thought that those who cultivate one field are not able to appreciate the labors of those who occupy themselves in the other. Indeed, it is usually accepted as a truth that to follow science with assiduity is practically sure to lead to unorthodoxy in religion. This is supposed to be especially true if the acquisition of scientific knowledge is pursued along lines that involve original research and new investigation. Somehow, it is thought that any one who has a mind free enough from the influence of prejudice and tradition to become an original thinker or investigator, is inevitably prone to abandon the old orthodox lines of thought in respect to religion.

Like a good many other convictions and persuasions that exist more or less as common-

3

places in the subconscious intellects of a great
many people, this is not true.   Our American
humorist said that it is not so much the ignorance of mankind that makes him ridiculous as
the knowing so many things "that ain't so."
The supposed opposition between science and religion is precisely an apposite type of one of the
things "that ain't so."   It is so firmly fixed as
a rule, however, that many people have accepted
it without being quite conscious of the fact that
it exists as one of the elements influencing many
of their judgments—a very important factor in
their apperception.

Now, it so happens that a number of prominent original investigators in modern science
were not only thoroughly orthodox in their religious beliefs, but were even faithful clergymen
and guiding spirits for others in the path of
Christianity.   The names of those who are in-
cluded in the present volume is the best proof of
this.   The series of sketches was written at various times, and yet there was a central thought
guiding the selection of the various scientific
workers.   Most of them lived at about the time
when, according to an unfortunate tradition that
has been very generally accepted, the Church
dominated human thinking so tyrannously as
practically to preclude all notion of original investigation in any line of thought, but especially
in matters relating to physical science.   Most of
the men whose lives are sketched lived during
the fifteenth, sixteenth, and first half of the seven-

teenth centuries. All of them were Catholic clergymen of high standing, and none of them suffered anything like persecution for his opinions; all remained faithful adherents of the Church through long lives.

It is hoped that this volume, without being in any sense controversial, may tend to throw light on many points that have been the subject of controversy; and by showing how absolutely free these great clergymen scientists were to pursue their investigations in science, it may serve to demonstrate how utterly unfounded is the prejudice that would declare that the ecclesiastical authorities of these particular centuries were united in their opposition to scientific advance.

There is no doubt that at times men have been the subject of persecution because of scientific opinions. In all of these cases, without exception, however—and this is particularly true of such men as Galileo, Giordano Bruno, and Michael Servetus—a little investigation of the personal character of the individuals involved in these persecutions will show the victims to have been of that especially irritating class of individuals who so constantly awaken opposition to whatever opinions they may hold by upholding them over-strenuously and inopportunely. They were the kind of men who could say nothing without, to some extent at least, arousing the resentment of those around them who still clung to older ideas. We all know this class of individual very well.

In these gentler modern times we may even be-
wail the fact that there is no such expeditious
method of disposing of him as in the olden time.
This is not a defence of what was done in their
regard, but is a word of explanation that shows
how human were the motives at work and how
unecclesiastical the procedures, even though
church institutions, Protestant and Catholic alike,
were used by the offended parties to rid them of
obnoxious argumentators.

In this matter it must not be forgotten that
persecution has been the very common associate
of noteworthy advances in science, quite apart
from any question of the relations between
science and religion. There has scarcely been a
single important advance in the history of applied science especially, that has not brought
down upon the devoted head of the discoverer,
for a time at least, the ill-will of his own generation. Take the case of medicine, for instance.
Vesalius was persecuted, but not by the ecclesiastical authorities. The bitter opposition to him
and to his work came from his colleagues in
medicine, who thought that he was departing
from the teaching of Galen, and considered that
a cardinal medical heresy not to be forgiven.
Harvey, the famous discoverer of the circulation
of the blood, lost much of his lucrative medical
practice after the publication of his discovery,
because his medical contemporaries thought the
notion of the heart pumping blood through the
arteries to be so foolish that they refused to

admit that it could come from a man of common sense, much less from a scientific physician. Nor need it be thought that this spirit of opposition to novelty existed only in the sixteenth and seventeenth centuries. Almost in our own time Semmelweis, who first taught the necessity for extreme cleanliness in obstetrical work, met with so much opposition in the introduction of the precautions he considered necessary that he was finally driven insane. His methods reduced the mortality in the great lying-in hospitals of Europe from nearly ten per cent for such cases down to less than one per cent, thus saving many thousands of lives every year.

Despite this very natural tendency to decry the value of new discoveries in science and the opposition they aroused, it will be found that the lives of these clergymen scientists show us that they met with much more sympathy in their work than was usually accorded to original investigators in science in other paths in life. This is so different from the ordinary impression in the matter that it seems worth while calling it to particular attention. While we have selected lives of certain of the great leaders in science, we would not wish it to be understood that these are the only ones among the clergymen of the last four centuries who deserve an honorable place high up in the roll of successful scientific investigators. Only those are taken who illustrate activity in sciences that are supposed to have been especially forbidden to clergymen. It has been said over and over again, for instance, that there was distinct ecclesiastical opposition to the study of chemistry. Indeed, many writers have not hesitated to say that there was a bull, or at least a decree, issued by one or more of the popes forbidding the study of chemistry. This is not only not true, but the very pope who is said to have issued the decree, John XXII, was himself an ardent student of the medical sciences. We still possess several books from him on these subjects, and his decree was meant only to suppress pseudo-science, which, as always, was exploiting the people for its own ends. The fact that a century later the foundation of modern chemical pharmacology was laid by a Benedictine monk, Basil Valentine, shows how unfounded is the idea that the papal decree actually hampered in any way the development of chemical investigation or the advance of chemical science.

Owing to the Galileo controversy, astronomy is ordinarily supposed to have been another of the sciences to which it was extremely indiscreet at least, not to say dangerous, for a clergyman to devote himself. The great founder of modern astronomy, however, Copernicus, was not only a clergyman, but one indeed so faithful and ardent that it is said to have been owing to his efforts that the diocese in which he lived did not go over to Lutheranism during his lifetime, as did most of the other dioceses in that part of Germany. The fact that Copernicus's book was involved in the Galileo trial has rendered his position still further misunderstood, but the matter is fully cleared up in the subsequent sketch of his life. As a matter of fact, it is in astronomy particularly that clergymen have always been in the forefront of advance; and it must not be forgotten that it was the Catholic Church that secured the scientific data necessary for the correction of the Julian Calendar, and that it was a pope who proclaimed the advisability of the correction to the world. Down to our own day there have always been very prominent clergymen astronomers. One of the best known names in the history of the astronomy of the nineteenth century is that of Father Piazzi, to whom we owe the discovery of the first of the asteroids. Other well-known names, such as Father Secchi, who was the head of the papal observatory at Rome, and Father Perry, the English Jesuit, might well be mentioned. The papal observatory at Rome has for centuries been doing some of the best work in astronomy accomplished anywhere, although it has always been limited in its means, has had inadequate resources to draw on, and has succeeded in accomplishing what it has done only because of the generous devotion of those attached to it.

To go back to the Galileo controversy for a moment, there seems no better answer to the assertion that his trial shows clearly the opposition between religion, or at least ecclesiastical authorities, and science, than to recall, as we have done, in writing the accompanying sketch of the

life of Father Kircher, S. J., that just after the
trial Roman ecclesiastics very generally were
ready to encourage liberally a man who devoted
himself to all forms of physical science, who
was an original thinker in many of them, who
was a great teacher, whose writings did more to
disseminate knowledge of advances in science
than those of any man of his time, and whose
idea of the collection of scientific curiosities into
a great museum at Rome (which still bears his
name) was one of the fertile germinal suggestions in which modern science was to find seeds
for future growth.

It is often asserted that geology was one of
the sciences that was distinctly opposed by
churchmen; yet we shall see that the father of
modern geology, one of the greatest anatomists
of his time, was not only a convert to Catholicity,
but became a clergyman about the time he was
writing the little book that laid the foundation
of modern geology. We shall see, too, that, far
from religion and science clashing in him, he
afterwards was made a bishop, in the hope that
he should be able to go back to his native land
and induce others to become members of that
Church wherein he had found peace and happi-
ness.

In the modern times biology has been supposed to be the special subject of opposition, or
at least fear, on the part of ecclesiastical authorities. It is for this reason that the life of Abbot
Mendel has been introduced. While working in

his monastery garden in the little town of Brünn in Moravia, this Augustinian monk discovered certain precious laws of heredity that are considered by progressive twentieth century scientists to be the most important contributions to the difficult problems relating to inheritance in biology that have been made.

These constitute the reasons for this little book on Catholic clergymen scientists. It is published, not with any ulterior motives, but simply to impress certain details of truth in the history of science that have been neglected in recent years and, by presenting sympathetic lives of great clergymen scientists, to show that not only is there no essential opposition between science and religion, but on the contrary that the quiet peace of the cloister and of a religious life have often contributed not a little to that precious placidity of mind which seems to be so necessary for the discovery of great, new scientific truths.

II.

COPERNICUS AND HIS TIMES.

ALL the vast and most progressive systems that human wisdom has brought forth as substitutes for religion, have never succeeded in interesting any but the learned, the ambitious, or at most the prosperous and happy. But the great majority of mankind can never come under these categories. The great majority of men are suffering, and suffering from moral as well as physical evils. Man's first bread is grief, and his first want is consolation. Now which of these systems has ever consoled an afflicted heart, or repeopled a lonely one? Which of these teachers has ever shown men how to wipe away a tear? Christianity alone has from the beginning promised to console man in the sorrows incidental to life by purifying the inclinations of his heart, and she alone has kept her promise.— MONTALEMBERT, Introduction to *Life of St. Elizabeth.*

NICOLAO COPERNICO

II.

COPERNICUS AND HIS TIMES.

THE association of the name of Copernicus with that of Galileo has always cast an air of unorthodoxy about the great astronomer. The condemnation of certain propositions in his work on astronomy in which Copernicus first set forth the idea of the universe as we know it at present, in contradistinction to the old Ptolemaic system of astronomy, would seem to emphasize this suspicion of unorthodox thinking. He is rightly looked upon as one of the great pioneers of our modern physical science, and, as it is generally supposed that scientific tendencies lead away from religion, there are doubtless many who look upon Copernicus as naturally one of the leaders in this rationalistic movement. It is forgotten that scarcely any of the great original thinkers have escaped the stigma of having certain propositions in some of their books condemned, and that this indeed is only an index of the fallibility of the human mind and of the need there is for some authoritative teacher. The sentences in Copernicus's book requiring correction were but few, and were rather matters of terminology than of actual perversion of accepted teaching. It was as such that their modification was suggested. In spite of this, the im-

15

pression remains that Copernicus must be considered as a rationalizing scientist, the first in a long roll of original scientific investigators whose work has made the edifice of Christianity totter by removing many of the foundation-stones of its traditional authority.

It is rather surprising, in view of this common impression with regard to Copernicus, to find him, according to recent biographers, a faithful clergyman in honor with his ecclesiastical superiors, a distinguished physician whose chief patients were clerical friends of prominent position and the great noblemen of his day, who not only retained all his faith and reverence for the Church, but seems to have been especially religious, a devoted adherent of the Blessed Virgin Mother of God, and the author of a series of poems in her honor that constitute a distinct contribution to the literature of his time.

All this should not be astonishing, however; for in the list of the churchmen of the half century just before the great religious revolt in Germany are to be found some of the best known names in the history of the intellectual development of the race. This statement is so contrary to the usual impression that obtains in regard to the character of that period as to be a distinct source of surprise to the ordinary reader of history who has the realization of its truth thrust upon him for the first time. Just before the so-called Reformation, the clergy are considered to have been so sunk in ignorance, or at least to have been so indifferent to intellectual pursuits and so cramped in mind as regards progress, or so timorous because of inquisition methods, that no great advances in thought, and especially not in science, could possibly be looked for from them. To find, then, that not only were faithful churchmen leaders in thought, discoverers in science, organizers in education, initiators of new progress, teachers of the New Learning, but that they were also typical representatives and yet prudent directors of the advancing spirit of that truly wonderful time, is apt to make us think that surely—as the Count de Maistre said one hundred years ago, and the Cambridge Modern History repeats at the beginning of the twentieth century when treating of this very period— "history has been a conspiracy against the truth."

Not quite fifty years before Luther's movement of protest began—that is, in 1471—there passed away in a little town in the Rhineland a man who has been a greater spiritual force than perhaps any other single man that has ever existed. This was Thomas à Kempis, a product of the schools of the Brethren of the Common Life, a teaching order that during these fifty years before the Protestant Revolution had over ten thousand pupils in its schools in the Rhineland and the Netherlands alone. As among these pupils there occur such names as Erasmus, Nicholas of Cusa, Agricola, not to mention many less illustrious, some idea of this old teaching institution, that has been very aptly compared to our modern Brothers of the Christian Schools, can be realized.

Kempis was a worthy initiator of a great half century. He had among his contemporaries, or followers in the next generation, such men as Grocyn, Dean Colet, and Linacre in England, Cardinal Ximenes in Spain, and Copernicus in Germany. Considering the usual impression in this matter as regards the lack of interest at Rome in serious study, it is curiously interesting to realize how closely these great scholars and thinkers were in touch with the famous popes of the Renaissance period. The second half of the sixteenth century saw the elevation to the papacy of some of the most learned and worthy men that have ever occupied the Chair of Peter. In 1447 Nicholas V became pope, and during his eight years of pontificate initiated a movement of sympathy with modern art and letters that was never to be extinguished. To him more than to any other may be attributed the foundation of the Vatican Library. To him also is attributed the famous expression that "no art can be too lofty for the service of the Church." He was succeeded by Calixtus III, a patron of learning, who was followed by Pius II, the famous Æneas Sylvius, one of the greatest scholars and most learned men of his day, who had done more for the spread of culture and of education in the various parts of Europe than perhaps any other alive at the time.

The next Pope, Paul II, accomplished much

during a period of great danger by arousing the
Christian opposition to the Saracens. His encouragement and material aid to the Hungarians,
who were making a bold stand against the Oriental invaders, merit for him a place in the rôle
of defenders of civilization. To him is due the
introduction of the recently discovered art of
printing and its installation on a sumptuous scale
worthy of the center of Christian culture. His
successor, Sixtus IV, deserves the title of the
founder of modern Rome. Bridges, aqueducts,
public buildings, libraries, churches—all owe to
his fostering care their restoration and renewed
foundation. He made it the purpose of his life
to attract distinguished humanistic scholars to
his capital, and Rome became the metropolis of
culture and learning as well as the mother city
of Christendom.

Under such popes it is no wonder that Rome
and the cities of Italy generally became the homes
of art and culture, centers of the new humanistic
learning and the shelters of the scholars of the
outer world. The Italian universities entered on
a period of intellectual and educational development as glorious almost as the art movement
that characterized the time. As this was marked
by the work of such men as that universal genius
Leonardo da Vinci, Michael Angelo, poet, painter,
sculptor, architect; Raphael, Titian, and Cor-
reggio, whose contemporaries were worthy of
them in every way, some idea can be attained of
the wonderful era that developed. No wonder

scholars in every department of learning flocked
to Italy for inspiration and the enthusiasm bred
of scholarly fellowship in such an environment.
From England came men like Linacre, Selling,
Grocyn, and Dean Colet; Erasmus came from
the Netherlands, and Copernicus from Poland.
Copernicus there obtained that scientific training
which was later to prove so fruitful in his practical work as a physician and in his scientific
work as the founder of modern astronomy.

It may be as well to say at the beginning that
even Copernicus was not the first to suggest that
the earth moved, and not the sun; and that, curiously enough, his anticipator was another church-
man, Nicholas of Cusa, the famous Bishop of
Brixen. Readers of Janssen's " History of the
German People " will remember that the distinguished historian introduces his monumental
work by a short sketch of the career of Cusanus,
as he is called, who may be well taken as the
typical pre-Reformation scholar and clergyman.
Cusa wrote in a manuscript—which is still preserved in the hospital of Cues, or Cusa—published for the first time by Professor Clemens in
1847: " I have long considered that this earth
can not be fixed, but moves as do the other stars
—sed movetur ut aliæ stellæ." What a curious
commentary these words, written more than half
a century before Galileo was born, form on the
famous expression so often quoted because supposed to have been drawn from Galileo by the
condemnation of his doctrine at Rome: E pur se

muove—" and yet it moves !" Cusanus was a Cardinal, the personal friend of three popes, and he seems to have had no hesitation in expressing his opinion in the matter. In the same manuscript the Cardinal adds: "And to my mind the earth revolves upon its axis once in a day and a night." Cusanus was, moreover, one of the most independent thinkers that the world has ever seen, yet he was intrusted by the pope about the middle of the fifteenth century with the reformation of abuses in the Church in Germany. The pope seems to have been glad to be able to secure a man of such straightforward ways for his reformatory designs.

The ideas of Nicholas of Cusa with regard to knowledge and the liberty of judgment in things not matters of faith can be very well appreciated from some of his expressions. " To know and to think," he says in one passage, " to see the truth with the eye of the mind is always a joy. The older a man grows, the greater is the pleasure it affords him ; and the more he devotes himself to the search after truth, the stronger grows his desire of possessing it. As love is the life of the heart, so is the endeavor after knowledge and truth the life of the mind. In the midst of the movements of time, of the daily work of life, of its perplexities and contradictions, we should lift our gaze fearlessly to the clear vault of heaven and seek ever to obtain a firmer grasp of, and keener insight into, the origin of all goodness and duty, the capacities of our own hearts and minds, the intellectual fruits of mankind throughout the centuries, and the wondrous works of nature around us; but ever remembering that in humility alone lies true greatness, and that knowledge and wisdom are alone profitable in so far as our lives are governed by them." [1] It is no wonder, then, that the time was ripe for Copernicus and his great work in astronomy, nor that that work should be accomplished while he was a canon of a cathedral and for a time the vicar-general of a diocese.

It is now nearly five years since Father Adolph Muller, S. J., professor of Astronomy in the Pontifical Gregorian University of Rome, and director of a private observatory on the Janiculum in that city, wrote his historical scientific study [2] of the great founder of modern astronomy. The book has been reviewed, criticized and discussed very thoroughly since then, and has been translated into several languages.   The latest translation was into Italian, the work of Father Pietro Mezzetti, S. J.,[3] and was published in Rome at the end of 1902—having had the benefit

---

[1] " History of the German People at the Close of the Middle Ages."   By Johannes Janssen. Translated from the German by M. A. Mitchell and A. M. Christie. Vol. I, p. 3.

[2] " Nikolaus Kopernicus, Der Altmeister der neueren Astronomie, Ein Lebens und Kultur Bild," von Adolf Muller, S. J.

[3] Professor of Astronomy and Physics at the Pontifical Leonine College of Anagni.

of the author's revision. The historical details, then, of Copernicus's life may be considered to have been cast into definite shape, and his career may be appreciated with confidence as to the absolute accuracy and essential significance of all its features.

Nicholas Copernicus—to give him the Latin and more usual form of his name — was the youngest of four children of Niclas Copernigk, who removed from Cracow in Poland to Thorn in East Prussia (though then a city of Poland), where he married Barbara Watzelrode, a daughter of one of the oldest and wealthiest families of the province. His mother's brother, after having been a canon for many years in the cathedral of Frauenburg, was elected Bishop of the Province of Ermland. The future astronomer was born in 1473, at a time when Thorn, after having been for over two hundred years under the rule of the Teutonic Knights, had for some seven years been under the dominion of the King of Poland. There were two boys and two girls in the family; and their fervent Catholicity can be judged from the fact that all of them, parents and children, were inscribed among the members of the Third Order of St. Dominic. Barbara, the older sister, became a religious in the Cistercian Convent of Kulm, of which her aunt Catherine was abbess, and of which later on she herself became abbess. Andrew, the oldest son, became a priest; and Nicholas, the subject of this sketch, at least assumed, as we shall see, all the

obligations of the ecclesiastical life, though it is
not certain that he received the major religious
orders.

Copernicus's collegiate education was obtained
at the University of Cracow, at that time one of
the most important seats of learning in Europe.
The five hundredth anniversary of the founding
of this University was celebrated with great
pomp only a few years ago. Its origin, however, dates back to the times of Casimir the Great,
at the end of the thirteenth or the beginning of
the fourteenth century. Its foundation was due
to the same spirit of enthusiastic devotion to
letters that gave us all the other great universities of the thirteenth century. The original institution was so much improved by Jagello, King
of Poland, at the beginning of the fifteenth century, that it bears his name and is known as the
Jagellonian University. It was very natural for
Copernicus to go back to his father's native city
for his education; but his ambitious spirit was
not content with the opportunities afforded there.
He does not seem to have taken his academic degrees, and the tradition that he received his doctorate in medicine at the University of Cracow
cannot be substantiated by any documentary evidence.

At Cracow, Copernicus devoted himself mainly
to classical studies, though his interest in astronomy seems to have been awakened there. In
fact, it is said that his desire to be able to read
Ptolemy's astronomy in the original Greek, and

to obtain a good copy of it, led him to look to Italy for his further education. During his years at Cracow, however, he seems to have made numerous observations in astronomy, as most of the astronomical data in his books are found reduced to the meridian of Cracow. The observatory of Frauenburg, at which his work in astronomy in later life was carried on, was on the same meridian; so that it is difficult to say, as have some of his biographers, that, since Cracow was the capital of his native country, motives of patriotism influenced him to continue his observations according to this same meridian. Copernicus was anxious, no doubt, to come in contact with some of the great astronomers at the universities of Italy, whom he knew by reputation and whose work was attracting attention all over Europe at that time.

How faithfully Copernicus applied himself to his classical studies can be best appreciated from some Latin poems written by him during his student days. These poems are an index, too, of the personal character of the man, and give some interesting hints of the religious side of his character. Altogether there are seven Latin odes, each ode composed of seven strophes. The seven odes are united by a certain community of interest or succession of subjects. All of them refer to the history of the Redeemer either in types or in reality. In the first one the prophets prefigure the appearance of the Saviour; in the second the patriarchs sigh for His coming; the

third depicts the scene of the Nativity in the
Cave of Bethlehem; the fourth is concerned with
the Circumcision and the imposition of the Name
chosen by the Holy Ghost; the fifth treats of the
Star and the Magi and their guidance to the
Manger; the sixth concerns the presentation in
the Temple; and the seventh, the scene in which
Jesus at the age of twelve disputes with the doctors in the Temple at Jerusalem.

Copernicus's recent biographers have called
attention particularly to the poetical beauties with
which he surrounds every mention of the Blessed
Virgin and her qualities. As is evident even
from our brief résumé of the subjects of the
odes, the themes selected are just those in which
the special devotion of the writer to the Mother
of the Saviour could be very well brought out.
There are, besides, a number of astronomical
allusions which stamp the poems as the work of
Copernicus, and which have been sufficient to
defend their authenticity against the attacks made
by certain critics, who tried to point out how
different was the style from that of Copernicus's
later years in his scientific writings. The tradition of authorship is, however, too well established on other grounds to be disturbed by criticism of this sort. The poems were dedicated to
the Pope. In writing poetry Copernicus was
only doing what Tycho Brahe and Kepler, his
great successors in astronomy, did after him;
and the argument with regard to the difference
of style in the two kinds of writings would hold
also as regards these authors.

Copernicus's years as a boy and man—that is, up to the age of thirty-five—corresponded with a time of great intellectual activity in Europe. This fact is not as generally recognized as it should be, for intellectual activity is supposed to have awakened after the so-called Reformation. During the years from 1472 to 1506, however, there were founded in Germany alone no less than six universities: those of Ingolstadt, Treves, Tübingen, Mentz, Wittenberg, and Frankfort-on-the-Oder. These were not by any means the first great institutions of learning that arose in Germany. The universities of Prague and Vienna were more than a century old, and, with Heidelberg, Cologne, Erfurt, Leipsic, and Rostock, besides Greifswald and Freiburg, founded about the middle of the fifteenth century, had reached a high state of development, and contained larger numbers of students, with few exceptions, than these same institutions have ever had down to our own day. In most cases their charters were derived from the pope; and most of the universities were actually recognized as ecclesiastical institutions, in the sense that their officials held ecclesiastical authority.

At this time—the end of the fifteenth and the beginning of the sixteenth century—it was not unusual for students, in their enthusiasm for learning, to attempt to exhaust nearly the whole round of university studies. Medicine seems to have been a favorite subject with scholars who were widely interested in knowledge for its own sake. Almost at the same time that Copernicus was studying in Italy, the distinguished English Greek scholar, Linacre, was also engaged in what would now be called post-graduate work at various Italian universities, and in the household of Lorenzo the Magnificent at Florence, with whose son—so much did Lorenzo think of him—he was allowed to study Greek. Linacre (as will be seen more at length in the sketch of his life in this volume), besides being the greatest Greek scholar of his time, the friend later of More and Colet and Erasmus in London, was also the greatest physician in England.

To those familiar with the times, it may be a source of surprise to think of Copernicus, interested as we know him to have been in literature and devoted so cordially to astronomy, yet taking up medicine as a profession. He seems, however, to have been led to do so by his distinguished teacher, Novara, who realized the talent of his Polish pupil for mathematics and astronomy and yet felt that he should have some profession in life. A century ago Coleridge, the English writer, said that a literary man should have some other occupation. Oliver Wendell Holmes improved upon this by adding: "And, as far as possible, he should confine himself to the other occupation." Novara seems to have realized that Copernicus might be under the necessity of knowing how to do something else besides making astronomical observations, in order to gain his living; and as medicine was satisfy-

ingly scientific, the old teacher suggested his taking it up as a profession. Copernicus made his
medical studies in Ferrara and Padua, and obtained his doctorate with honors from Ferrara.

Copernicus seems to have taken up the practice of his profession seriously, and to have per-
severed in it to the end of his life. His biographers say that in the exercise of his professional
duties he was animated by the spirit of a person
who had devoted himself to the ecclesiastical life.
While he did not publicly practise his profession,
he was ever ready to assist the poor; and he also
acquired great reputation in the surrounding
country for his medical attendance upon clerics
of all ranks. This continued to be the case, notwithstanding the fact that after the death of his
uncle his mother inherited considerable wealth,
and the family circumstances changed so much
that he might well have given up any labors that
were meant only to add to his income. In a
word, he seems to have had a sincere interest in
his professional work, and to have continued its
exercise because of the opportunities it afforded
for the satisfaction of a mind devoted to scientific research.

Copernicus acquired considerable reputation
by his medical services. His friend Giese speaks
of him as a very skilful physician, and even calls
him a second Æsculapius. Maurice Ferber, who
became Bishop of Ermland in 1523, suffered
from a severe chronic illness that began about
1529. He obtained permission from the canons

of the cathedral to have Doctor Copernicus, whose ability and zeal he never ceased to praise, to come from the cathedral town where he ordinarily resided to Heilsburg, in order to have him near him. Bishop Ferber's successor, Dantisco, also secured Copernicus's aid in a severe illness, and declared that his restoration to health was mainly due to the efforts of his learned physician. Giese was so confident of the Doctor's skill that when he became Bishop of Kulm and on one of his episcopal visitations fell ill at a considerable distance from Copernicus's place of residence, he insisted on having the astronomer doctor brought to take care of him.

In 1541 Duke Albert of Prussia became very much worried over the illness of one of his most trusted counsellors. In his distress he had recourse to Copernicus, and his letter asking the Canon of the Cathedral of Frauenburg to come to attend the patient is still extant. He says that the cure of the illness is "very much at his heart"; and, as every other means has failed, he hopes Copernicus will do what he can for the assistance of his faithful and valued counsellor. Copernicus yielded to the request, and the counsellor began to improve shortly after his arrival. At the end of some weeks the Duke wrote again to the canons of the cathedral asking that the leave of absence granted to Copernicus should be extended in order to enable him to complete the cure which had been so happily begun. In this second letter the Duke talks of Copernicus as a

most skilful and learned physician. At the end
of the month there is a third letter from the
Duke, in which he thanks all the canons of the
cathedral for their goodness in having granted
the desired permission, and he adds that he shall
ever feel under obligations " for the assistance
rendered by that very worthy and excellent physician, Nicholas Copernicus, a doctor who is de-
serving of all honor." Not long afterward,
when Copernicus's book on astronomy was published, a copy of it was sent to the Duke, and he
replied that he was deeply grateful for it, and
that he should always preserve it as a souvenir
of the most learned and gentlest of men.

There are a number of notes on the art of
medicine made by Copernicus in the books of the
cathedral library at Frauenburg. They serve to
show how faithful a student he was, and to a
certain extent give an idea of the independent
habit of mind which he brought to the investigation of medicine as well as to the study of astronomy. Unfortunately, these have not as yet found
an editor; but it is to be hoped that we shall
soon know more of the medical thinking of a
man over whose mind tradition, in the unworthier.
sense of that word, exercised so little influence.

In 1530 Copernicus wrote a short prelude to
the longer work on astronomy which he was to
publish later. The propositions contained in this
work show how far he had advanced on the road
to his ultimate discovery. After a few words of
introduction, the following seven axioms are laid
down :—

1. The celestial spheres and their orbits have not a single center.

2. The center of the earth is not the center of the universe, but only the center of gravity and of the moon's orbit.

3. The planes of the orbits lie around the sun, which may be considered as the center of the universe.

4. The distance from the earth to the sun compared with that from the earth to the fixed stars is extremely small.

5. The daily motion of the heavenly sphere is apparent—that is, it is an effect of the rotary motion of the earth upon its axis.

6. The apparent motions of the moon and of the sun are so different because of the effect produced by the motion of the earth.

7. The movements of the earth account for the apparent retrograde motion and other irregularities of the movements of the planets. It is enough to assume that the earth alone moves, in order to explain all the other movements observed in the heavens.

It is no wonder that one of his bishop-friends, Frisio, writing to another bishop-friend, Dantisco, said: " If Copernicus succeeds in demonstrating the truth of his thesis—and we may well consider that he will from this prelude—he will give us a new heaven and a new earth." This shorter exposition of Copernicus's views was found in manuscript in the imperial library in Vienna only about a quarter of a century ago.

It is mentioned by Tycho Brahe in one of his works on astronomy in which he reviews the various contemporary advances made in the knowledge of the heavens.

The publication of Copernicus's great work, "De Revolutionibus Orbium Celestium," was delayed until he was advanced in years, because his astronomical opinions were constantly progressing; and, with the patience of true genius, he was not satisfied with anything less than the perfect expression of truth as he saw it. It has sometimes been said that it was delayed because Copernicus feared the storm of religious persecution which he foresaw it would surely arouse. How utterly without foundation is this pretence, which has unfortunately crept into serious history, can be seen from the fact that Pope Paul III accepted the dedication of the work; and of the twelve popes who immediately followed Paul not one even thought of proceeding against Copernicus's work. His teaching was never questioned by any of the Roman Congregations for nearly one hundred years after his death. Galileo's injudicious insistence in his presentation of Copernicus's doctrine, on the novelties of opinion that controverted long-established beliefs, was then responsible for the condemnation by the Congregation of the Index; and, as we shall see, this was not absolute, but only required that certain passages should be corrected. The corrections demanded were unimportant as regards the actual science, and

merely insisted that Copernicus's teaching was
hypothesis and not yet actual demonstration.

It must not be forgotten, after all, that the
reasons advanced by Copernicus for his idea of
the movements of the planets were not supported
by any absolute demonstration, but only by reasons from analogy. Nearly a hundred years
later than his time, even after the first discoveries
had been made by the newly constructed tele-
scopes, in Galileo's day, there was no absolute
proof of the true system of the heavens. The
famous Jesuit astronomer, Father Secchi, says
the reasons adduced by Galileo were no real
proofs : they were only certain analogies, and by
no means excluded the possibility of the contrary
propositions with regard to the movements of
the heavens being true. "None of the real
proofs for the earth's rotation upon its axis were
known at the time of Galileo, nor were there
direct conclusive arguments for the earth's moving around the sun." Even Galileo himself confessed that he had not any strict demonstration
of his views, such as Cardinal Bellarmine re-
quested. He wrote to the Cardinal, "The system seems to be true;" and he gave as a reason
that it corresponded to the phenomena.

According to the astronomers of the time,
however, the old Ptolemaic system, in the shape
in which it was explained by the Danish astronomer Tycho Brahe, who was acknowledged as
the greatest of European astronomers, appeared
to give quite a satisfactory explanation of the

phenomena observed. The English philosopher, Lord Bacon, more than a decade after Galileo's announcement, considered that there were certain phenomena in nature contrary to the Copernican theory, and so he rejected it altogether. This was within a few years of the condemnation by the Congregation at Rome. As pointed out by Father Heinzle, S. J., in his article on Galileo in the "Catholic World" for 1887, "science was so far from determining the question of the truth or falsity of either the Ptolemaic or the Copernican system that shortly before 1633, the year of Galileo's condemnation, a number of savants, such as Fromond in Louvain, Morin in Paris, Berigard in Pisa, Bartolinus in Copenhagen, and Scheiner in Rome, wrote against Copernicanism."

As we have said, Copernicus's book was not condemned unconditionally by the Roman authorities, but only until it should be corrected. This assured protection to the principal part of the work, and the warning issued by the Roman Congregation in the year 1820 particularizes the details that had to be corrected. It is interesting to note that whenever Copernicus is spoken of in this Monitum it is always in flattering terms as a "noble astrologer"—the word astrologer having at that time no unworthy meaning. The whole work is praised and its scientific quality acknowledged.

The passages requiring correction were not many. In the first book, at the beginning of the fifth chapter, Copernicus made the declaration that " the immobility of the earth was not a decided question, but was still open to discussion." In place of these words it was suggested that the following should be inserted: " In order to explain the apparent motions of the celestial bodies, it is a matter of indifference whether we admit that the earth occupies a place in the middle of the heavens or not."

In the eighth chapter of the first book, Copernicus said: " Why, then, this repugnance to concede to our globe its own movement as natural to it as is its spherical form? Why prefer to make the whole heavens revolve around it, with the great danger of disturbance that would result, instead of explaining all these apparent movements of the heavenly bodies by the real rotation of the earth, according to the words of Æneas, ' We are carried from the port, and the land and the cities recede '?" This passage was to be modified as follows: " Why not, then, admit a certain mobility of the earth corresponding to its form, since the whole universe of which we know the bounds is moved, producing appearances which recall to the mind the well-known saying of Æneas in Virgil, ' The land and the cities recede '?"

Toward the end of the same chapter Copernicus, continuing the same train of thought, says: " I do not fear to add that it is incomparably more unreasonable to make the immense vault of the heavens revolve than to admit the revolu-

tion of our little terrestrial globe." This passage was to be modified as follows: "In one
case as well as in the other—that is, whether we
admit the rotation of the earth or that of the
heavenly spheres—we encounter the same difficulties."

The ninth chapter of the first book begins with
these words: "There being no difficulty in ad-
mitting, then, the mobility of the earth, let us
proceed to see whether it has one or a number
of movements, and whether, therefore, our earth
is a simple planet like the other planets." The
following words were to be substituted: "Sup-
posing, then, that the earth does move, it is
necessary to examine whether this movement is
multiple or not."

Toward the middle of the tenth chapter Copernicus declares: "I do not hesitate to defend the
proposition that the earth, accompanied by the
moon, moves around the sun;" while the word-
ing of this proposition had to be changed so as
to substitute the term "admit" for "defend."
The title of the eleventh chapter, "Demonstration of the Triple Movement of the Earth," was
modified to read as follows: "The Hypothesis
of the Triple Movement of the Earth, and the
Reasons Therefor." The title of the twentieth
chapter of the fourth book originally read: "On
the Size of the Three Stars [*Sidera*], the sun,
the moon, and the earth." The word "stars"
was removed from this title, the earth not being
considered as a star. The concluding words of

the tenth chapter of the first book, " So great is
the magnificent work of the Omnipotent Artif-
icer," had to be cancelled, because they expressed
an assurance of the truth of his system not war-
ranted by knowledge. With these few unimportant changes, any one might read and study
Copernicus's work with perfect freedom.

Traditions to the contrary notwithstanding,
Galileo, because of the friendship and encouragement of the churchmen in Italy, had been placed
in conditions eminently suited for study and investigation. Several popes and a number of
prominent ecclesiastics were his constant friends
and patrons. The perpetual secretary of the
Paris Academy of Sciences, M. Bertrand, himself a great mathematician and historian, declares that the long life of Galileo was one of the
most enviable that is recorded in the history of
science. "The tale of his misfortunes has confirmed the triumph of the truth for which he
suffered. Let us tell the whole truth. This
great lesson was learned without any profound
sorrow to Galileo; and his long life, considered
as a whole, was one of the most serene and enviable in the history of science."

Copernicus, like Galileo, had clerical friends
to thank for an environment that proved the
greatest possible aid to his scientific work. His
position as Canon of the Cathedral of Frauenburg provided him with learned leisure, while
his clerical friends took just enough interest in
his investigations and the preliminary announce-

ments of his discoveries to make his pursuit of
astronomical studies to some definite conclusion
a worthy aim in life. It was this assistance that
enabled him to publish his book eventually and
bring his great theory before the world.

Copernicus, far from having any leanings toward the so-called " reform " movement (as has
often been asserted), was evidently a staunch
supporter of his friend and patron Bishop
Maurice Ferber, of Ermland, who kept his see
loyal to Rome at a time when the secularization
of the Teutonic order and the falling away of
many bishops all around him make his position
as a faithful son of the Church and that of his
diocese noteworthy in the history of that time
and place. It may well be said that under less
favorable conditions Copernicus's work might
never have been finished. As it was, his book
met with great opposition from the Reformers,
but remained absolutely acceptable even to the
most rigorous churchmen until Galileo's unfortunate insistence on the points of it that were
opposed to generally accepted theories.

During all his long life Copernicus remained
one of the simplest of men. Genius as he was,
he could not have failed to realize how great was
the significance of the discoveries he had made
in astronomy. In spite of this he continued to
exercise during a long career the simple duties
of his post as Canon of the Cathedral of Frauen-
berg, nor did he fail to give such time as was
asked of him for the medical treatment of the

poor or of his friends, the ecclesiastics of the
neighborhood. These duties—as he seems to
have considered them—must have taken many
precious hours from his studies, but they were
given unstintingly. When he came to die, his
humility was even more prominent than during
life. It was at his own request that there was
graven upon his tombstone simply the prayer,
" I ask not the grace accorded to Paul, not that
given to Peter: give me only the favor Thou
didst show to the thief on the cross." There is
perhaps no better example in all the world of the
simplicity of true genius nor any better example
of how sublimely religious may be the soul that
has far transcended the bounds of the scientific
knowledge of its own day.

The greatness of Copernicus's life-work can
best be realized from the extent to which he
surpassed even well-known contemporaries in
astronomy and from his practical anticipation of
the opinions of some of his greatest successors.
Even Tycho Brahe, important though he is in
the history of astronomical science, taught many
years after Copernicus's death the doctrine that
the earth is the center of the universe. Newton
had in Copernicus a precursor who divined the
theory of universal gravitation; and even Kepler's great laws, especially the elliptical form of
the orbits of the planets, are at least hinted at
in Copernicus's writings. He is certainly one of
the most original geniuses of all times; and it is
interesting to find that the completeness of his

scholarly career, far from being rendered abortive by friction with ecclesiastical superiors, as we might imagine probable from the traditions that hang around his name, was rather made possible by the sympathy and encouragement of clerical friends and church authorities. Copernicus the scholar, astronomer, physician, and clergyman, is a type of the eve of the Reformation period, and his life is the best possible refutation of the slanders with regard to the unprogressiveness of the Church and churchmen of that epoch which have unfortunately been only too common in the histories of the time.

III.

BASIL VALENTINE, FOUNDER OF MODERN CHEMISTRY.

L ET us, then, banish into the world of fiction that affirmation so long repeated by foolish credulity which made monasteries an asylum for indolence and incapacity, for misanthropy and pusillanimity, for feeble and melancholic temperaments, and for men who were no longer fit to serve society in the world. Monasteries were never intended to collect the invalids of the world. It was not the sick souls, but on the contrary the most vigorous and healthful the human race has ever produced who presented themselves in crowds to fill them. — MONTALEMBERT, *Monks of the West*.

III.

BASIL VALENTINE, FOUNDER OF MODERN CHEMISTRY.

THE Protestant tradition which presumes a priori that no good can possibly have come out of the Nazareth of the times before the Reformation, and especially the immediately preceding century, has served to obscure to an unfortunate degree the history of several hundred years extremely important in every department of education. Strange as it may seem to those unfamiliar with the period, it is in that department which is supposed to be so typically modern—the physical sciences—that this neglect is most serious. Such a hold has this Protestant tradition on even educated minds that it is a source of great surprise to most people to be told that there were in many parts of Europe original observers in the physical sciences all during the thirteenth, fourteenth, and fifteenth centuries who were doing ground-breaking work of the highest value, work that was destined to mean much for the development of modern science. Speculations and experiments with regard to the philosopher's stone and the transmutation of metals are supposed to fill up all the interests of the alchemists of those days. As a matter of fact, however, men were making original observations of very

45

profound significance, and these were considered
so valuable by their contemporaries that, though
printing had not yet been invented, even the immense labor involved in copying large folio volumes by hand did not suffice to deter them from
multiplying the writings of these men and thus
preserving them for future generations, until the
printing-press came to perpetuate them.

At the beginning of the twentieth century,
with some of the supposed foundations of modern chemistry crumbling to pieces under the influences of the peculiarly active light thrown
upon older chemical theories by the discovery of
radium and the radio-active elements generally,
there is a reawakening of interest in some of
the old-time chemical observers whose work used
to be laughed at as so unscientific and whose
theory of the transmutation of elements into one
another was considered so absurd. The idea
that it would be impossible under any circumstances to convert one element into another belongs entirely to the nineteenth century. Even
so distinguished a mind as that of Newton, in
the preceding century, could not bring itself to
acknowledge the modern supposition of the ab-
surdity of metallic transformation, but, on the
contrary, believed very firmly in this as a basic
chemical principle and confessed that it might be
expected to occur at any time. He had seen
specimens of gold ores in connexion with metallic copper, and had concluded that this was a
manifestation of the natural transformation of
one of these yellow metals into the other.

With the discovery that radium transforms itself into helium, and that indeed all the so-called radio-activities of the very heavy metals are probably due to a natural transmutation process constantly at work, the ideas of the older chemists cease entirely to be a subject for amusement. The physical chemists of the present day are very ready to admit that the old teaching of the absolute independence of something over seventy elements is no longer tenable, except as a working hypothesis. The doctrine of matter and form taught for so many centuries by the scholastic philosophers which proclaimed that all matter is composed of two principles, an underlying material substratum and a dynamic or informing principle, has now more acknowledged veri-similitude, or lies at least closer to the generally accepted ideas of the most progressive scientists, than it has at any time for the last two or three centuries. Not only the great physicists, but also the great chemists, are speculating along lines that suggest the existence of but one form of matter, modified according to the energies that it possesses under a varying physical and chemical environment. This is, after all, only a re-statement in modern terms of the teaching of St. Thomas of Aquin in the thirteenth century.

It is not surprising, then, that there should be a reawakening of interest in the lives of some of the men who, dominated by the earlier scholastic ideas and by the tradition of the possibility of finding the philosopher's stone, which would

transmute the baser metals into the precious
metals, devoted themselves with quite as much
zeal as any modern chemist to the observation of
chemical phenomena.   One of the most interesting of these—indeed he might well be said to be
the greatest of the alchemists—is the man whose
only name that we know is that which appears
on a series of manuscripts written in the High
German dialect of the end of the fifteenth and
the beginning of the sixteenth century.   That
name is Basil Valentine, and the writer, according to the best historical traditions, was a Benedictine monk.   The name Basil Valentine may
only have been a pseudonym, for it has been impossible to trace it among the records of the
monasteries of the time.   That the writer was a
monk there seems to be no doubt, for his writings in manuscript and printed form began to
have their vogue at a time when there was little
likelihood of their being attributed to a monk
unless an indubitable tradition connected them
with some monastery.

This Basil Valentine (to accept the only name
we have), as we can judge very well from his
writings, eminently deserves the designation of
the last of the alchemists and the first of the
chemists.   There is practically a universal recognition of the fact now that he deserves also the
title of Founder of Modern Chemistry, not only
because of the value of the observations contained in his writings, but also because of the
fact that they proved so suggestive to certain

scientific genuises during the century succeeding
Valentine's life. Almost more than to have
added to the precious heritage of knowledge for
mankind is it a boon for a scientific observer to
have awakened the spirit of observation in others
and to be the founder of a new school of thought.
This Basil Valentine undoubtedly did.

Besides, his work furnishes evidence that the
investigating spirit was abroad just when it is
usually supposed not to have been, for the Thur-
ingian monk surely did not do all his investigating alone, but must have received as well as
given many a suggestion to his contemporaries.

In the history of education there are two com-
monplaces that are appealed to oftener than any
other as the sources of material with regard to
the influence of the Catholic Church on education during the centuries preceding the Reformation. These are the supposed idleness of the
monks, and the foolish belief in the transmutation of metals and the search for the philosopher's stone which dominated the minds of so
many of the educated men of the time. It is in
Germany especially that these two features of
the pre-Reformation period are supposed to be
best illustrated. In recent years, however, there
has come quite a revolution in the feelings even
of those outside of the Church with regard to
the proper appreciation of the work of the monastic scholars of these earlier centuries. Even
though some of them did dream golden dreams
over their alembics, the love of knowledge meant

more to them, as to the serious students of any
age, than anything that might be made by it.
As for their scientific beliefs, if there can be a
conversion of one element into another, as seems
true of radium, then the possibility of the transmutation of metals is not so absurd as, for a century or more, it has seemed; and it is not impossible that at some time even gold may be
manufactured out of other metallic materials.

Of course, a still worthier change of mind has
come over the attitude of educators because of
the growing sense of appreciation for the wonderful work of the monks of the Middle Ages,
and even of those centuries that are supposed to
show least of the influence of these groups of
men who, forgetting material progress, devoted
themselves to the preservation and the cultivation of the things of the spirit. The impression
that would consider the pre-Reformation monks
in Germany as unworthy of their high calling in
the great mass is almost entirely without foundation. Obscure though the lives of most of
them were, many of them rose above their environment in such a way as to make their work
landmarks in the history of progress for all time.

Because their discoveries are buried in the old
Latin folios that are contained only in the best
libraries, not often consulted by the modern
scientist, it is usually thought that the scientific
investigators of these centuries before the Reformation did no work that would be worth while
considering in our present day. It is only some

one who goes into this matter as a labor of love
who will consider it worth his while to take the
trouble seriously to consult these musty old
tomes. Many a scholar, however, has found his
labor well rewarded by the discovery of many
an anticipation of modern science in these volumes so much neglected and where such treasure-
trove is least expected. Professor Clifford Allbutt, the Regius Professor of physics at the University of Cambridge, in his address on " The
Historical Relations of Medicine and Surgery
Down to the End of the Sixteenth Century,"
which was delivered at the St. Louis Congress
of Arts and Sciences during the Exposition in
1904, has shown how much that is supposed to
be distinctly modern in medicine, and above all
in surgery, was the subject of discussion at the
French and Italian universities of the thirteenth
century. William Salicet, for instance, who
taught at the University of Bologna, published
a large series of case histories, substituted the
knife for the Arabic use of the cautery, described
the danger of wounds of the neck, investigated
the causes of the failure of healing by first in-
tention, and sutured divided nerves. His pupil,
Lanfranc, who taught later at the University of
Paris, went farther than his master by distinguishing between venous and arterial hemorrhage, requiring digital compression for an hour
to stop hemorrhage from the *venae pulsatiles*—
the pulsating veins, as they were called—and if
this failed because of the size of the vessel, sug-

gesting the application of a ligature. Lanfranc's chapter on injuries to the head still remains a noteworthy book in surgery that establishes beyond a doubt how thoughtfully practical were these teachers in the medieval universities. It must be remembered that at this time all the teachers in universities, even those in the medical schools as well as those occupied with surgery, were clerics. Professor Allbutt calls attention over and over again to this fact, because it emphasizes the thoroughness of educational methods, in spite of the supposed difficulties that would lie in the way of an exclusively clerical teaching staff.

In chemistry the advances made during the thirteenth, fourteenth, and fifteenth centuries were even more noteworthy than those in any other department of science. Albertus Magnus, who taught at Paris, wrote no less than sixteen treatises on chemical subjects, and, notwithstanding the fact that he was a theologian as well as a scientist and that his printed works filled sixteen folio volumes, he somehow found the time to make many observations for himself and performed numberless experiments in order to clear up doubts. The larger histories of chemistry accord him his proper place and hail him as a great founder in chemistry and a pioneer in original investigation.

Even St. Thomas of Aquin, much as he was occupied with theology and philosophy, found some time to devote to chemical questions. After all, this is only what might have been expected of the favorite pupil of Albertus Magnus. Three treatises on chemical subjects from Aquinas's pen have been preserved for us, and it is to him that we are said to owe the origin of the word amalgam, which he first used in describing various chemical methods of metallic combination with mercury that were discovered in the search for the genuine transmutation of metals.

Albertus Magnus's other great scientific pupil, Roger Bacon, the English Franciscan friar, followed more closely in the physical scientific ways of his great master. Altogether he wrote some eighteen treatises on chemical subjects. For a long time it was considered that he was the inventor of gunpowder, though this is now known to have been introduced into Europe by the Arabs. Roger Bacon studied gunpowder and various other explosive combinations in considerable detail, and it is for this reason that he obtained the undeserved reputation of being an original discoverer in this line. How well he realized how much might be accomplished by means of the energy stored up in explosives can perhaps be best appreciated from the fact that he suggested that boats would go along the rivers and across the seas without either sails or oars and that carriages would go along the streets without horse or man power. He considered that man would eventually invent a method of harnessing these explosive mixtures and of utilizing their energies for his purposes without

danger. It is curiously interesting to find, as
we begin the twentieth century, and gasolene is
so commonly used for the driving of automo-
biles and motor boats and is being introduced
even on railroad cars in the West as the most
available source of energy for suburban traffic,
that this generation should only be fulfilling the
idea of the old Franciscan friar of the thirteenth
century, who prophesied that in explosives there
was the secret of eventually manageable energy
for transportation purposes.

Succeeding centuries were not as fruitful in
great scientists as the thirteenth, and yet at the
beginning of the fourteenth there was a pope,
three of whose scientific treatises—one on the
transmutation of metals, which he considers an
impossibility, at least as far as the manufacture
of gold and silver was concerned; a treatise on
diseases of the eyes, of which Professor Allbutt [1]
says that it was not without its distinctive practical value, though compiled so early in the history of eye surgery; and, finally, his treatise on
the preservation of the health, written when he
was himself over eighty years of age—are all
considered by good authorities as worthy of the
best scientific spirit of the time. This pope was
John XXII, of whom it has been said over and
over again by Protestant historians that he issued
a bull forbidding chemistry, though he was himself one of the enthusiastic students of chemistry

[1] Address cited.

in his younger years and always retained his interest in the science.[1]

During the fourteenth century Arnold of Villanova, the inventor of nitric acid, and the two Hollanduses kept up the tradition of original investigation in chemistry. Altogether there are some dozen treatises from these three men on chemical subjects. The Hollanduses particularly did their work in a spirit of thoroughly frank, original investigation. They were more interested in minerals than in any other class of substances, but did not waste much time on the question of transmutation of metals. Professor Thompson, the professor of chemistry at Edinburgh, said in his history of chemistry many years ago that the Hollanduses have very clear descriptions of their processes of treating minerals in investigating their composition, which serve to show that their knowledge was by no means entirely theoretical or acquired only from books or by argumentation.

Before the end of this fourteenth century, according to the best authorities on this subject, Basil Valentine, the more particular subject of our essay, was born.

Valentine's career is a typical example of the personally obscure but intellectually brilliant lives

[1] For the refutation of this calumny with regard to John XXII, see " Pope John XXII and the supposed Bull forbidding Chemistry," by James J. Walsh, Ph. D., LL. D., in the Medical Library and Historical Journal, October, 1905.

which these old monks lived. It seems probable, according to the best authorities, as we have said, that his work began shortly before the middle of the fifteenth century, although most of what was important in it was accomplished during the second half. It would not be so surprising, as most people who have been brought up to consider the period just before the Reformation in Germany as wanting in progressive scholars might imagine, for a supremely great original investigator to have existed in North Germany about this time. After all, before the end of the century, Copernicus, the Pole, working in northern Germany, had announced his theory that the earth was not the center of the universe, and had set forth all that this announcement meant. To a bishop-friend who said to him, "But this means that you are giving us a new universe," he replied that the universe was already there, but his theory would lead men to recognize its existence. In southern Germany, Thomas à Kempis, who died in 1471, had traced for man the outlines of another universe, that of his own soul, from its mystically practical side. These great Germans were only the worthy contemporaries of many other German scholars scarcely less distinguished than these supreme geniuses. The second half of the fifteenth century, the beginning of the Renaissance in Germany as well as Italy, is that wonderful time in history when somehow men's eyes were opened to see farther and their minds broadened to gather in more of the truth of man's relation to the universe, than had ever before been the case in all the centuries of human existence, or than has ever been possible even in these more modern centuries, though supposedly we are the heirs of all the ages in the foremost files of time.

Coming as he did before printing, when the spirit of tradition was even more rife and dominating than it has been since, it is almost needless to say that there are many curious legends associated with the name of Basil Valentine. Two centuries before his time, Roger Bacon, doing his work in England, had succeeded in attracting so much attention even from the common people, because of his wonderful scientific discoveries, that his name became a by-word and many strange magical feats were attributed to him. Friar Bacon was the great wizard even in the plays of the Elizabethan period. A number of the same sort of myths attached themselves to the Benedictine monk of the fifteenth century. He was proclaimed in popular story to have been a wonderful magician. Even his manuscript, it was said, had not been published directly, but had been hidden in a pillar in the church attached to the monastery and had been discovered there after the splitting open of the pillar by a bolt of lightning from heaven. It is the extension of this tradition that has sometimes led to the assumption that Valentine lived in an earlier century, some even going so far as to say that he, too, like Roger Bacon, was a product of the thirteenth century. It seems reasonably possible, however, to separate the traditional from what is actual in his existence, and thus to obtain some idea at least of his work, if not of the details of his life. The internal evidence from his works enable the historian of science to place him within a half century of the discovery of America.

One of the stories told with regard to Basil Valentine, because it has become a commonplace in philology, has made him more generally known than any of his actual discoveries. In one of the most popular of the old-fashioned text-books of chemistry in use a quarter of a century ago, in the chapter on Antimony, there was a story that I suppose students never forgot. It was said that Basil Valentine, a monk of the Middle Ages, was the discoverer of this substance. After having experimented with it in a number of ways, he threw some of it out of his laboratory one day, where the swine of the monastery, finding it, proceeded to gobble it up together with some other refuse. He watched the effect upon the swine very carefully, and found that, after a preliminary period of digestive disturbance, these swine developed an enormous appetite and became fatter than any of the others. This seemed a rather desirable result, and Basil Valentine, ever on the search for the practical, thought that he might use the remedy to good purpose even on the members of the community.

Now, some of the monks in the monastery were of rather frail health and delicate constitution, and he thought that the putting on of a little fat in their case might be a good thing. Accordingly he administered, surreptitiously, some of the salts of antimony, with which he was experimenting, in the food served to these monks. The result, however, was not so favorable as in the case of the hogs. Indeed, according to one, though less authentic, version of the story, some of the poor monks, the unconscious subjects of the experiment, even perished as the result of the ingestion of the antimonial compounds. According to the better version they suffered only the usual unpleasant consequences of taking antimony, which are, however, quite enough for a fitting climax to the story. Basil Valentine called the new substance which he had discovered antimony, that is, opposed to monks. It might be good for hogs, but it was a form of monks' bane, as it were.[1]

[1] It is curious to trace how old are the traditions on which some of these old stories that must now be rejected, are founded. I have come upon the story with regard to Basil Valentine and the antimony and the monks in an old French medical encyclopedia of biography, published in the seventeenth century, and at that time there was no doubt at all expressed as to its truth. How much older than this it may be I do not know, though it is probable that it comes from the sixteenth century, when the *kakoethes scribendi* attacked many people because of the facility of printing, and when most of the good stories that have so worried the modern dry-as-dust historian in his researches for their correction became a part of the body of supposed historical tradition.

Unfortunately for most of the good stories of history, modern criticism has nearly always failed to find any authentic basis for them, and they have had to go the way of the legends of Washington's hatchet and Tell's apple. We are sorry to say that that seems to be true also of this particular story. Antimony, the word, is very probably derived from certain dialectic forms of the Greek word for the metal, and the name is no more derived from *anti* and *monachus* than it is from *anti* and *monos* (opposed to single existence), another fictitious derivation that has been suggested, and one whose etymological value is supposed to consist in the fact that antimony is practically never found alone in nature.

Notwithstanding the apparent cloud of unfounded traditions that are associated with his name, there can be no doubt at all of the fact that Valentinus—to give him the Latin name by which he is commonly designated in foreign literatures—was one of the great geniuses who, working in obscurity, make precious steps into the unknown that enable humanity after them to see things more clearly than ever before. There are definite historical grounds for placing Basil Valentine as the first of the series of careful observers who differentiated chemistry from the old alchemy and applied its precious treasures of information to the uses of medicine. It was because of the study of Basil Valentine's work that Paracelsus broke away from the Galenic traditions, so supreme in medicine up to his time, and began our modern pharmaceutics. Following on the heels of Paracelsus came Van Helmont, the father of modern medical chemistry, and these three did more than any others to enlarge the scope of medication and to make observation rather than authority the most important criterion of truth in medicine. Indeed, the work of these three men dominated medicine, or at least the department of pharmaceutics, down almost to our own day, and their influence is still felt in drug-giving.

While we do not know the absolute date of either the birth or the death of Basil Valentine and are not sure even of the exact period in which he lived and did his work, we are sure that a great original observer about the time of the invention of printing studied mercury and sulphur and various salts, and above all, introduced antimony to the notice of the scientific world, and especially to the favor of practitioners of medicine. His book, "The Triumphal Chariot of Antimony," is full of conclusions not quite justified by his premises nor by his observations. There is no doubt, however, that the observational methods which he employed did give an immense amount of knowledge and formed the basis of the method of investigation by which the chemical side of medicine was to develop during the next two or three centuries. Great harm was done by the abuse of antimony, but then great harm is done by the abuse of anything, no matter how good it may be. For a time it came to be the most important drug in medicine and was only replaced by venesection.

The fact of the matter is that doctors were looking for effects from their drugs, and antimony is, above all things, effective. Patients, too, wished to see the effect of the medicines they took. They do so even yet, and when antimony was administered there was no doubt about its working.

Some five years ago, when Sir Michael Foster, M. D., professor of physiology in the University of Cambridge, England, was invited to deliver the Lane lectures at the Cooper Medical College, in San Francisco, he took for his subject "The History of Physiology." In the course of his lecture on "The Rise of Chemical Physiology" he began with the name of Basil Valentine, who first attracted men's attention to the many chemical substances around them that might be used in the treatment of disease, and said of him:—

He was one of the alchemists, but in addition to his inquiries into the properties of metals and his search for the philosopher's stone, he busied himself with the nature of drugs, vegetable and mineral, and with their action as remedies for disease. He was no anatomist, no physiologist, but rather what nowadays we should call a pharmacologist. He did not care for the problem of the body, all he sought to understand was how the constituents of the soil and of plants might be treated so as to be available for healing the sick and how they produced their effects. We apparently owe to him the introduction of many chemical substances, for instance, of hydrochloric acid, which he prepared from oil of vitriol and salt, and of many vegetable drugs. And he was apparently the author of certain conceptions which, as we shall see, played an important part in the development of chemistry and of physiology. To him, it seems, we owe the idea of the three "elements," as they were and have been called, replacing the old idea of the ancients of the four elements—earth, air, fire, and water. It must be remembered, however, that both in the ancient and in the new idea the word "element" was not intended to mean that which it means to us now, a fundamental unit of matter, but a general quality or property of matter. The three elements of Valentine were (1) sulphur, or that which is combustible, which is changed or destroyed, or which at all events disappears during burning or combustion ; (2) mercury, that which temporarily disappears during burning or combustion, which is dissociated in the burning from the body burnt, but which may be recovered, that is to say, that which is volatile, and (3) salt, that which is fixed, the residue or ash which remains after burning.

The most interesting of Basil Valentine's books, and the one which has had the most enduring influence, is undoubtedly "The Triumphal Chariot of Antimony." It has been translated and has had a wide vogue in every language of modern Europe. Its recommendation of antimony had such an effect upon medical practice that it continued to be the most important drug in the pharmacopœia down almost to the middle of the nineteenth century. If any proof were needed that Basil Valentine or that the author of the books that go under that name was a monk, it would be found in the introduction to this volume, which not only states that fact very clearly, but also in doing so makes use of language that shows the writer to have been deeply imbued with the old monastic spirit. I quote the first paragraph of this introduction in order to make clear what I mean. The quotation is taken from the English translation of the work as published in London in 1678. Curiously enough, seeing the obscurity surrounding Valentine himself, we do not know for sure who made the translation. The translator apologizes somewhat for the deeply religious spirit of the book, but considers that he was not justified in eliminating any of this. Of course, the translation is left in the quaint old-fashioned form so eminently suited to the thoughts of the old master, and the spelling and use of capitals is not changed :

Basil Valentine : His Triumphant Chariot of Antimony.—Since I, Basil Valentine, by Religious Vows am bound to live according to the Order of St. Benedict, and that requires another manner of spirit of Holiness than the common state of Mortals exercised in the profane business of this World ; I thought it my duty before all things, in the beginning of this little book, to declare what is necessary to be known by the pious Spagyrist [old-time name for medical chemist], inflamed with an ardent desire of this Art, as what he ought to do, and whereunto to direct his aim, that he may lay such foundations of the whole matter as may be stable ; lest his Building, shaken with the Winds, happen to fall, and the whole Edifice to be involved in shameful Ruine, which otherwise, being founded on more firm and solid principles, might have continued for a long series of time. Which Admonition I judged was, is and always will be a necessary part of my Religious Office ; especially since we must all die, and no one of us which are now, whether high or low, shall long be seen among the number of men. For it concerns me to recommend these Meditations of Mortality to Posterity, leaving them behind me, not only that honor may be given to the Divine Majesty, but also that Men may obey him sincerely in all things.

In this my Meditation I found that there were five principal heads, chiefly to be considered by the wise and prudent spectators of our Wisdom and Art. The first of which is, Invocation of God. The second, Contemplation of Nature. The third, True Preparation. The fourth, the Way of Using. The fifth, Utility and Fruit. For he who regards not these, shall never obtain place among true Chymists, or fill up the number of perfect Spagyrists. Therefore, touching these five heads, we shall here following treat and so far declare them, as that the general Work may be brought to light and perfected by an intent and studious Operator.

This book, though the title might seem to indicate it, is not devoted entirely to the study of antimony, but contains many important additions to the chemistry of the time. For instance, Basil Valentine explains in this work how what he calls the spirit of salt might be obtained. He succeeded in manufacturing this material by treating common salt with oil of vitriol and heat. From the description of the uses to which he put the end product of his chemical manipulation, it is evident that under the name of spirit of salt

he is describing what we now know as hydrochloric acid. This is the first definite mention of
it in the history of science, and the method suggested for its preparation is not very different
from that employed even at the present time.
He also suggests in this volume how alcohol may
be obtained in high strengths. He distilled the
spirit obtained from wine over carbonate of
potassium, and thus succeeded in depriving it of
a great proportion of its water.

We have said that he was deeply interested in
the philosopher's stone. Naturally this turned
his attention to the study of metals, and so it is
not surprising to find that he succeeded in for-
mulating a method by which metallic copper
could be obtained. The substance used for the
purpose was copper pyrites, which was changed
to an impure sulphate of copper by the action
of oil of vitriol and moist air. The sulphate of
copper occurred in solution, and the copper could
be precipitated from it by plunging an iron bar
into it. Basil Valentine recognized the presence
of this peculiar yellow metal and studied some
of its qualities. He does not seem to have been
quite sure, however, whether the phenomenon
that he witnessed was not really a transmutation
of the iron into copper, as a consequence of the
other chemicals present.

There are some observations on chemical physiology, and especially with regard to respiration,
in the book on antimony which show their author
to have anticipated the true explanation of the

theory of respiration. He states that animals breathe, because the air is needed to support their life, and that all the animals exhibit the phenomenon of respiration. He even insists that the fishes, though living in water, breathe air, and he adduces in support of this idea the fact that whenever a river is entirely frozen the fishes die. The reason for this being, according to this old-time physiologist, not that the fishes are frozen to death, but that they are not able to obtain air in the ice as they did in the water, and consequently perish.

There are many testimonies to the practical character of all his knowledge and his desire to apply it for the benefit of humanity. The old monk could not repress the expression of his impatience with physicians who gave to patients for diseases of which they knew little, remedies of which they knew less. For him it was an unpardonable sin for a physician not to have faithfully studied the various mixtures that he prescribed for his patients, and not to know not only their appearance and taste and effect, but also the limits of their application. Considering that at the present time it is a frequent source of complaint that physicians often prescribe remedies with whose physical appearances they are not familiar, this complaint of the old-time chemist alchemist will be all the more interesting for the modern physician. It is evident that when Basil Valentine allows his ire to get the better of him it is because of his indignation over the quacks who were abusing medicine and patients in his time, as they have ever since. There is a curious bit of aspersion on mere book-learning in the passage that has a distinctly modern ring, and one feels the truth of Russell Lowell's expression that to read a great genius, no matter how antique, is like reading a commentary in the morning paper, so up-to-date does genius ever remain :—

And whensoever I shall have occasion to contend in the School with such a Doctor, who knows not how himself to prepare his own medicines, but commits that business to another, I am sure I shall obtain the Palm from him; for indeed that good man knows not what medicines he prescribes to the sick; whether the color of them be white, black, grey, or blew, he cannot tell; nor doth this wretched man know whether the medicine he gives be dry or hot, cold or humid; but he only knows that he found it so written in his Books, and thence pretends knowledge (or as it were, Possession) by Prescription of a very long time; yet he desires to further Information.   Here again let it be lawful to exclaim, Good God, to what a state is the matter brought! what goodness of minde is in these men! what care do they take of the sick!   Wo, wo to them! in the day of Judgment they will find the fruit of their ignorance and rashness, then they will see Him whom they pierced, when they neglected their Neighbor, sought after money and nothing else; whereas were they cordial in their profession, they would spend Nights and Days in Labour that they might become more learned in their Art, whence more certain health would accrew to the sick with their Estimation and greater glory to themselves.

But since Labour is tedious to them, they commit the matter to chance, and being secure of their Honour, and content with their Fame, they (like Brawlers) defend themselves with a certain garrulity, without any respect had to Confidence or Truth.

Perhaps one of the reasons why Valentine's book has been of such enduring interest is that it is written in an eminently human vein and out of a lively imagination. It is full of figures relating to many other things besides chemistry, which serve to show how deeply this investigating observer was attentive to all the problems of life around him. For instance, when he wants to describe the affinity that exists between many substances in chemistry, and which makes it impossible for them not to be attracted to one another, he takes a figure from the attractions that he sees exist among men and women. There are some paragraphs with regard to the influence of the passion of love that one might think rather a quotation from an old-time sermon than from a great ground-breaking book in the science of chemistry.

Love leaves nothing entire or sound in man; it impedes his sleep; he cannot rest either day or night; it takes off his appetite that he hath no disposition either to meat or drink by reason of the continual torments of his heart and mind. It deprives him of all Providence, hence he neglects his affairs, vocation and business. He minds neither study, labor nor prayer; casts away all thoughts of anything but the body beloved; this is his study, this his most vain occupation. If to lovers

the success be not answerable to their wish, or so soon
and prosperously as they desire, how many melancholies
henceforth arise, with griefs and sadnesses, with which
they pine away and wax so lean as they have scarcely
any flesh cleaving to the bones.   Yea, at last they lose
the life itself, as may be proved by many examples! for
such men, (which is an horrible thing to think of) slight
and neglect all perils and detriments, both of the body
and life, and of the soul and eternal salvation.

It is evident that human nature is not different
in our sophisticated twentieth century from that
which this observant old monk saw around him
in the fifteenth.   He continues:—

How many testimonies of this violence which is in
love, are daily found? for it not only inflames the
younger sort, but it so far exaggerates some persons far
gone in years as through the burning heat thereof, they
are almost mad.   Natural diseases are for the most part
governed by the complexion of man and therefore in-
vade some more fiercely, others more gently; but Love,
without distinction of poor or rich, young or old, seizeth
all, and having seized so blinds them as forgetting all
rules of reason, they neither see nor hear any snare.

But then the old monk thinks that he has said
enough about this subject and apologizes for his
digression in another paragraph that should remove any lingering doubt there may be with regard to the genuineness of his monastic character.   The personal element in his confession is
so naïve and so simply straightforward that instead of seeming to be the result of conceit, and
so repelling the reader, it rather attracts his

kindly feeling for its author. The paragraph would remind one in certain ways of that personal element that was to become more popular in literature after Montaigne had made such extensive use of it.

But of these enough; for it becomes not a religious man to insist too long upon these cogitations, or to give place to such a flame in his heart. Hitherto (without boasting I speak it) I have throughout the whole course of my life kept myself safe and free from it, and I pray and invoke God to vouchsafe me his Grace that I may keep holy and inviolate the faith which I have sworn, and live contented with my spiritual spouse, the Holy Catholick Church. For no other reason have I alleaged these than that I might express the love with which all tinctures ought to be moved towards metals, if ever they be admitted by them into true friendship, and by love, which permeates the inmost parts, be converted into a better state.

The application of the figure at the end of his long digression is characteristic of the period in which he wrote and to a considerable extent also of the German literary methods of the time.

In this volume on the use of antimony there are in most of the editions certain biographical notes which have sometimes been accepted as authentic, but oftener rejected. According to these, Basil Valentine was born in a town in Alsace, on the southern bank of the Rhine. As a consequence of this, there are several towns that have laid claim to being his birthplace. M. Jean Reynaud, the distinguished French philosophical writer of the first half of the nineteenth century, once said that Basil Valentine, like Ossian and Homer, had many towns claim him years after his death. He also suggested that, like those old poets, it was possible that the writings sometimes attributed to Basil Valentine were really the work not of one man, but of several individuals. There are, however, many objections to this theory, the most forceful of which is the internal evidence of the books themselves and their style and method of treatment. Other biographic details contained in " The Triumphal Chariot of Antimony " are undoubtedly more correct. According to them, Basil Valentine travelled in England and Holland on missions for his order, and went through France and Spain on a pilgrimage to St. James of Compostella.

Besides this work, there is a number of other books of Basil Valentine's, printed during the first half of the sixteenth century, that are well-known and copies of which may be found in most of the important libraries. The United States Surgeon General's Library at Washington contains several of the works on medical subjects, and the New York Academy of Medicine Library has some valuable editions of his works. Some of his other well-known books, each of which is a good-sized octavo volume, bear the following descriptive titles (I give them in English, though, as they are usually to be found, they are in Latin, sixteenth century trans-

lations of the original German): " The World
in Miniature: or, The Mystery of the World
and of Human Medical Science," published at
Marburg, 1609;—" The Chemical Apocalypse:
or, The Manifestation of Artificial Chemical
Compounds," published at Erfurt in 1624;—"A
Chemico Philosophic Treatise Concerning Things
Natural and Preternatural, Especially Relating
to the Metals and the Minerals," published at
Frankfurt in 1676;—" Haliography: or, The
Science of Salts: A Treatise on the Prepara-
tion, Use and Chemical Properties of All the
Mineral, Animal and Vegetable Salts," published
at Bologna in 1644;—" The Twelve Keys of
Philosophy," Leipsic, 1630.

The great interest manifested in Basil Valentine's work at the Renaissance period can be best
realized from the number of manuscript copies
and their wide distribution. His books were not
all printed at one place, but, on the contrary, in
different portions of Europe. The original edition of " The Triumphal Chariot of Antimony "
was published at Leipsic in the early part of the
sixteenth century. The first editions of the other
books, however, appeared at places so distant
from Leipsic as Amsterdam and Bologna, while
various cities of Germany, as Erfurt and Frankfurt, claim the original editions of still other
works. Many of the manuscript copies still exist
in various libraries in Europe; and while there
is no doubt that some unimportant additions to
the supposed works of Basil Valentine have come

from the attribution to him of scientific treatises
of other German writers, the style and the
method of the principal works mentioned is entirely too similar not to have been the fruit of a
single mind and that possessed of a distinct investigating genius setting it far above any of its
contemporaries in scientific speculation and observation.

The most interesting feature of all of Basil
Valentine's writings that are extant is the distinctive tendency to make his observations of
special practical utility. His studies in antimony
were made mainly with the idea of showing how
that substance might be used in medicine. He
did not neglect to point out other possible uses,
however, and knew the secret of the employment
of antimony in order to give sharpness and defi-
nition to the impression produced by metal types.
It would seem as though he was the first scientist who discussed this subject, and there is even
some question whether printers and type founders did not derive their ideas in this matter
from Basil Valentine, rather than he from them.
Interested as he was in the transmutation of
metals, he never failed to try to find and suggest
some medicinal use for all of the substances that
he investigated. His was no greedy search for
gold and no accumulation of investigations with
the idea of benefiting only himself. Mankind
was always in his mind, and perhaps there is no
better demonstration of his fulfilment of the
character of the monk than this constant solici-

tude to benefit others by every bit of investigation that he carried out. For him with medieval nobleness of spirit the first part of every work must be the invocation of God, and the last, though no less important than the first, must be the utility and fruit for mankind that can be derived from it.

IV.

LINACRE: SCHOLAR, PHYSICIAN, PRIEST.

L INACRE, as Dr. Payne remarks, "was possessed from his youth till his death by the enthusiasm of learning. He was an idealist devoted to objects which the world thought of little use." Painstaking, accurate, critical, hypercritical perhaps, he remains to-day the chief literary representative of British Medicine. Neither in Britain nor in Greater Britain have we maintained the place in the world of letters created for us by Linacre's noble start. Quoted by OSLER in *Æquanimitas*.

THOMAS LINACRE

IV.

LINACRE: SCHOLAR, PHYSICIAN, PRIEST.

NOT long ago, in one of his piquant little essays, Mr. Augustine Birrell discussed the question as to what really happened at the time of the so-called Reformation in England. There is much more doubt with regard to this matter, even in the minds of non-Catholics, than is usually suspected. Mr. Birrell seems to have considered it one of the most important problems, and at the same time not by any means the least intricate one, in modern English history. The so-called High Church people emphatically insist that there is no break in the continuity of the Church of England, and that the modern Anglicanism is a direct descendant of the old British Church. They reject with scorn the idea that it was the Lutheran movement on the Continent which brought about the changes in the Anglican Church at that time. Protestantism did not come into England for a considerable period after the change in the constitution of the Anglican Church, and when it did come its tendencies were quite as subversal of the authority of the Anglican as of the Roman Church. Protestantism is the mother of Nonconformism in England. It can be seen, then, that the question as to what did really take place in the time

of Henry VIII and of Edward VI is still open.
It has seemed to me that no little light on this
vexed historical question will be thrown by a
careful study of the life of Dr. Linacre, who,
besides being the best known physician of his
time in England, was the greatest scholar of the
English Renaissance period, yet had all his life
been on very intimate terms with the ecclesiastical authorities, and eventually gave up his
honors, his fortune, and his profession to become a simple priest of the old English Church.

Considering the usually accepted notions as to
the sad state of affairs supposed to exist in the
Church at the beginning of the sixteenth century,
this is a very remarkable occurrence, and deserves careful study to determine its complete
significance, for it tells better than anything else
the opinion of a distinguished contemporary.
Few men have ever been more highly thought of
by their own generation. None has been more
sincerely respected by intimate friends, who were
themselves the leaders of the thought of their
generation, than Thomas Linacre, scholar, physician and priest; and his action must stand as the
highest possible tribute to the Church in England at that time.

How unimpaired his practical judgment of
men and affairs was at the time he made his
change from royal physician to simple priest can
best be gathered from the sagacity displayed in
the foundation of the Royal College of Physicians, an institution he was endowing with the

wealth he had accumulated in some twenty years of most lucrative medical practice. The Royal College of Physicians represents the first attempt to secure the regulation of the practice of medicine in England, and, thanks to its founder's wonderful foresight and practical wisdom, it remains down to our own day, under its original constitution, one of the most effective and highly honored of British scientific foundations. No distinction is more sought at the present time by young British medical men, or by American or even Continental graduates in medicine, than the privilege of adding to their names the letters " F. R. C. P. (Eng.)," Fellow of the Royal College of Physicians of England. The College worked the reformation of medical practice in England, and its methods have proved the suggestive formulæ for many another such institution and for laws that all over the world protect, to some extent at least, the public from quacks and charlatans.

Linacre's change of profession at the end of his life has been a fruitful source of conjecture and misconception on the part of his biographers. Few of them seem to be able to appreciate the fact, common enough in the history of the Church, that a man may, even when well on in years, give up everything to which his life has been so far directed, and from a sense of duty devote himself entirely to the attainment of " the one thing necessary." Linacre appears only to have done what many another in the history of

the thirteenth, fourteenth, and fifteenth centuries
did without any comment; but his English biographers insist on seeing ulterior motives in it, or
else fail entirely to understand it.   The same
action is not so rare even in our own day that it
should be the source of misconception by later
writers.

Dr. S. Weir Mitchell has, in the early part of
" Dr. North and His Friends," a very curious
passage with regard to Linacre.   One of the
characters, St. Clair, says: " I saw, the other
day, at Owen's, a life of one Linacre, a doctor,
who had the luck to live about 1460 to 1524,
when men knew little and thought they knew all.
In his old age he took for novelty to reading St.
Matthew.   The fifth, sixth, and seventh chapters
were enough.   He threw the book aside and
cried out, ' Either this is not the Gospel, or we
are not Christians.'   What else could he say?"
St. Clair uses the story to enforce an idea of his
own, which he states as a question, as follows:
"And have none of you the courage to wrestle
with the thought I gave you, that Christ could
not have expected the mass of men to live the
life He pointed out as desirable for the first dis-
ciples of His faith?"

Dr. Mitchell's anecdote is not accepted by Linacre's biographers generally, though it is copied
by Dr. Payne, the writer of the article on Linacre in the (English) " Dictionary of National
Biography," who, however, discredits it somewhat.   The story is founded on Sir John Cheke's

account of the conversion of Linacre. It is very doubtful, however, whether Linacre's deprecations of the actions of Christians had reference to anything more than the practice of false swearing so forcibly denounced in the Scriptures, which had apparently become frequent in his time. This is Selden's version of the story as quoted by Dr. Johnson, who was Linacre's well-known biographer. Sir John Cheke in his account seems to hint that this chance reading of the Scriptures represented the first occasion Linacre had ever taken of an opportunity to read the New Testament. Perhaps we are expected to believe that, following the worn-out Protestant tradition of the old Church's discouraging of the reading of the Bible, and of the extreme scarcity of copies of the Book, this was the first time he had ever had a good opportunity to read it. This, of course, is nonsense.

Linacre's early education had been obtained at the school of the monastery of Christ Church at Canterbury, and the monastery schools all used the New Testament as a text-book, and as the offices of the day at which the students were required to attend contain these very passages from Matthew which Linacre is supposed to have read for the first time later in life, this idea is preposterous. Besides, Linacre, as one of the great scholars of his time, intimate friend of Sir Thomas More, of Dean Colet, and Erasmus, can scarcely be thought to find his first copy of the Bible only when advanced in years. This is evi-

dently a post-Reformation addition, part of the
Protestant tradition with regard to the supposed
suppression of the Scriptures in pre-Reformation
days, which every one acknowledges now to be
without foundation.

Linacre, as many another before and since,
seems only to have realized the true significance
of the striking passages in Matthew after life's
experiences and disappointments had made him
take more seriously the clauses of the Sermon
on the Mount.   There is much in fifth, sixth,
and seventh Matthew that might disturb the com-
placent equanimity of a man whose main objects
in life, though pursued with all honorable un-
selfishness, had been the personal satisfaction of
wide scholarship and success in his chosen profession.

With regard to Sir John Cheke's story, Dr.
John Noble Johnson, who wrote the life of
Thomas Linacre,[1] which is accepted as the
authoritative biography by all subsequent writers,
says: " The whole statement carries with it an
air of invention, if not on the part of Cheke
himself, at least on that of the individual from
whom he derives it, and it is refuted by Lin-

[1] " The Life of Thomas Linacre," Doctor in Medi-
cine, Physician to King Henry VIII, the Tutor and
Friend of Sir Thomas More and the Founder of the
College of Physicians in London.   By John Noble John-
son, M. D., late Fellow of the Royal College of Physi-
cians, London.   Edited by Robert Graves, of the Inner
Temple, Barrister at Law.   London: Edward Lumley,
Chancery Lane.   1835.

acre's known habits of moderation and the many ecclesiastical friendships which, with a single exception, were preserved without interruption until his death. It was a most frequent mode of silencing opposition to the received and established tenets of the Church, when arguments were wanting, to brand the impugner with the opprobrious titles of heretic and infidel, the common resource of the enemies to innovation in every age and country."

The interesting result of the reflections inspired in Linacre by the reading of Matthew was, as has been said, the resignation of his high office of Royal Physician and the surrender of his wealth for the foundation of chairs in Medicine and Greek at Oxford and Cambridge. With the true liberal spirit of a man who wished to accomplish as much good as possible, his foundations were not limited to his own University of Oxford. After these educational foundations, however, his wealth was applied to the endowment of the Royal College of Physicians and its library, and to the provision of such accessories as might be expected to make the College a permanently useful institution, though left at the same time perfectly capable of that evolution which would suit it to subsequent times and the development of the science and practice of medicine.

It is evident that the life of such a man can scarcely fail to be of personal as well as historic interest.

Thomas Linacre was born about 1460—the year is uncertain—at Canterbury. Nothing is known of his parents or their condition, though this very silence in their regard would seem to indicate that they were poor and obscure. His education was obtained at the school of the monastery of Christ Church, Canterbury, then presided over by the famous William Selling, the first of the great students of the new learning in England. Selling's interest seems to have helped Linacre to get to Oxford, where he entered at All Souls' College in 1480. In 1484 he was elected a Fellow of the College, and seems to have distinguished himself in Greek, to which he applied himself with special assiduity under Cornelio Vitelli. Though Greek is sometimes spoken of as having been introduced into Western Europe only at the beginning of the sixteenth century, Linacre undoubtedly laid the foundation of that remarkable knowledge of the language which he displayed at a later period of his life, during his student days at Oxford in the last quarter of the fifteenth century.

Linacre went to Italy under the most auspicious circumstances. His old tutor and friend at Canterbury, Selling, who had become one of the leading ecclesiastics of England, was sent to Rome as an Ambassador by Henry VII. He took Linacre with him. A number of English scholars had recently been in Italy and had attracted attention by their geniality, by their thorough-going devotion to scholarly studies,

and by their success in their work. Selling himself had made a number of firm friends among
the Italian students of the New Learning on a
former visit, and they now welcomed him with
enthusiasm and were ready to receive his pro-
tégé with goodwill and provide him with the
best opportunities for study. As a member of
the train of the English ambassador, Linacre had
an entrée to political circles that proved of great
service to him, and put him on a distinct footing
above that of the ordinary English student in
Italy.

Partly because of these and partly because of
his own interesting and attractive personal character, Linacre had a number of special opportunities promptly placed at his disposal. Church
dignitaries in Rome welcomed him and he was
at once received into scholarly circles wherever
he went in Italy. Almost as soon as he arrived
in Florence, where he expected seriously to take
up the study of Latin and Greek, he became the
intimate friend of the family of Lorenzo de'
Medici, who was so charmed with his personality
and his readily recognizable talent that he chose
him for the companion of his son's studies and
received him into his own household.

Politian was at this time the tutor of the
young de' Medici in Latin, and Demetrius Chal-
condylas the tutor in Greek. Under these two
eminent scholars Linacre obtained a knowledge
of Latin and Greek such as it would have been
impossible to have obtained under any other cir-

cumstances, and which with his talents at once
stamped him as one of the foremost humanistic
scholars in Europe. While in Florence he came
in contact with Lorenzo the Magnificent's
younger son, who afterwards became Leo X.
The friendship thus formed lasted all during
Linacre's lifetime, and later on he dedicated at
least one of his books to Alexander de' Medici
after the latter's elevation to the papal throne.

It is no wonder that Linacre always looked
back on Italy as the Alma Mater — the fond
mother in the fullest sense of the term—to whom
he owed his precious opportunities for education
and the broadest possible culture. In after-life
the expression of his feelings was often tinged
with romantic tenderness. It is said that when
he was crossing the Alps, on his homeward journey, leaving Italy after finishing his years of
apprenticeship of study, standing on the highest
point of the mountains from which he could still
see the Italian plains, he built with his own
hands a rough altar of stone and dedicated it to
the land of his studies—the land in which he had
spent six happy years—under the fond title of
Sancta Mater Studiorum.

At first, after his return from Italy, Linacre
lectured on Greek at Oxford. Something of the
influence acquired over English students and the
good he accomplished may be appreciated from
the fact that with Grocyn he had such students
as More and the famous Dean Colet. Erasmus
also was attracted from the Netherlands and

studied Greek under Linacre, to whom he refers in the most kindly and appreciative terms many times in his after life. Linacre wrote books besides lecturing, and his work on certain fine points in the grammar of classical Latinity proved a revelation to English students of the old classical languages, for nothing so advanced as this had ever before been attempted outside Italy. In one of the last years of the fifteenth century Linacre was appointed tutor to Prince Arthur, the elder brother of Henry VIII, to whom it will be remembered that Catherine of Aragon had been betrothed before her marriage with Henry. Arthur's untimely death, however, soon put an end to Linacre's tutorship.

As pointed out by Einstein, the reputation of Grocyn and Linacre was not confined to England, but soon spread all over the Continent. After the death of the great Italian humanists of the fifteenth century, who had no worthy successors in the Italian peninsula, these two men became the principal European representatives of the New Learning. There were other distinguished men, however, such as Vives, the Spaniard; Lascaris, the Greek; Buda, or Budæus, the Frenchman, and Erasmus, whom we have already mentioned—all of whom joined at various times in praising Linacre.

Some of Linacre's books were published by the elder Aldus at Venice; and Aldus is even said to have sent his regrets on publishing his edition of Linacre's translation of " The Sphere of Proclus," that the distinguished English humanist had not forwarded him others of his works to print. Aldus appreciatively added the hope that the eloquence and classic severity of style in Linacre's works and in those of the English humanists generally " might shame the Italian philosophers and scholars out of their uncultured methods of writing."

Augusta Theodosia Drane (Mother Raphael), in her book on " Christian Schools and Scholars," gives a very pleasant picture of how Dean Colet, Erasmus, and More used at this time to spend their afternoons down at Stepney (then a very charming suburb of London), of whose parish church Colet was the vicar. They stopped at Colet's house and were entertained by his mother, to whom we find pleasant references in the letters that passed between these scholars. Linacre was also often of the party, and the conversations between these greatest students and literary geniuses of their age would indeed be interesting reading, if we could only have had preserved for us, in some way, the table-talk of those afternoons. Erasmus particularly was noted for his wit and for his ability to turn aside any serious discussions that might arise among his friends, so as to prevent anything like unpleasant argument in their friendly intercourse. A favorite way seems to have been to insist on telling one of the old jokes from a classic author whose origin would naturally be presumed to be much later than the date the New Learning had found for it.

Dean Colet's mother appears to have been much more than merely the conventional hostess. Erasmus sketches her in her ninetieth year with her countenance still so fair and cheerful that you would think she had never shed a tear. Her son tells in some of his letters to Erasmus and More of how much his mother liked his visitors and how agreeable she found their talk and witty conversation. They seem to have appreciated her in turn, for in Mother Raphael's chapter on English Scholars of the Renaissance there is something of a description of her garden, in which were to be found strawberries, lately brought from Holland, some of the finer varieties of which Mrs. Colet possessed through Erasmus's acquaintance in that country. Mrs. Colet also had some of the damask roses that had lately been introduced into England by Linacre, who was naturally anxious that the mother of his friend should have the opportunity to raise some of the beautiful flowers he was so much interested in domesticating in England.

It is a very charming picture, this, of the early humanists in England, and very different from what might easily be imagined by those unfamiliar with the details of the life of the period. Linacre was later to give up his worldly emoluments and honors and become a clergyman, in order to do good and at the same time satisfy his own craving for self-abnegation. More was to rise to the highest positions in England, and then for conscience' sake was to suffer death rather than yield to the wishes of his king in a matter in which he saw principle involved. Dean Colet himself was to be the ornament of the English clergy and the model of the scholar clergyman of the eve of the Reformation, to whom many generations were to look back as a worthy object of reverence. Erasmus was to become involved first with and then against Luther, and to be offered a cardinal's hat before his death. His work, like Newman's, was done entirely in the intellectual field. Meantime, in the morning of life, all of them were enjoying the pleasures of friendly intercourse and the charms of domestic felicity under circumstances that showed that their study of humanism and their admiration for the classics impaired none of their sympathetic humanity or their appreciation of the innocent delights of the present.

For us, however, Linacre's most interesting biographic details are those which relate to medicine, for, besides his humanistic studies while in Italy, Linacre graduated in medicine, obtaining the degree of doctor at Padua. The memory of the brilliant disputation which he sustained in the presence of the medical faculty in order to obtain his degree is still one of the precious traditions in the medical school of Padua. He does not seem to have considered his medical education finished, however, by the mere fact of having obtained his doctor's degree, and there is a tradition of his having studied later at Vicenza under Nicholas Leonicenus, the most celebrated physician and scholar in Italy at the end of the fifteenth century, who many years afterwards referred with pardonable pride to the fact that he had been Linacre's teacher in medicine.

It may seem strange to many that Linacre, with all his knowledge of the classics, should have devoted himself for so many years to the study of medicine in addition to his humanistic studies. It must not be forgotten, however, that the revival of the classics of Latin and Greek brought with it a renewed knowledge of the great Latin and Greek fathers of medicine, Hippocrates and Galen. This had a wonderful effect in inspiring the medical students of the time with renewed enthusiasm for the work in which they were engaged. A knowledge of the classics led to the restoration of the study of anatomy, botany, and of clinical medicine, which had been neglected in the midst of application to the Arabian writers in medicine during the preceding centuries. The restoration of the classics made of medicine a progressive science in which every student felt the possibility of making great discoveries that would endure not only for his own reputation but for the benefit of humanity.

These thoughts seem to have attracted many promising young men to the study of medicine. The result was a period of writing and active observation in medicine that undoubtedly makes this one of the most important of literary medical eras. Some idea of the activity of the writers of the time can be gathered from the important

medical books — most of them large folios —
which were printed during the last half of the
sixteenth century in Italy. There is a series of
these books to be seen in one of the cases of the
library of the Surgeon-General at Washington,
which, though by no means complete, must be a
source of never-ending surprise to those who are
apt to think of this period as a *saison morte* in
medical literature.

There must have been an extremely great interest in medicine to justify all this printing.
Some of the books are among the real incunabula
of the art of printing. For instance, in 1474
there was published at Bologna De Manfredi's
" Liber de Homine;" at Venice, in 1476, Petrus
de Albano's work on medicine; and in the next
twenty years from the same home of printing
there came large tomes by Angelata, a translation of Celsus, and Aurelius Cornelius and
Articellus's " Thesaurus Medicorum Veterum,"
besides several translations of Avicenna and Pla-
tina's work " De Honesta Voluptate et Valetu-
dine." At Ferrara, Arculanus's great work was
published, while at Modena there appeared the
" Hortus Sanitatis," or Garden of Health, whose
author was J. Cuba. There were also translations from other Arabian authors on medicine in
addition to Avicenna, notably a translation of
Rhazes Abu Bekr Muhammed Ben Zankariah
Abrazi, a distinguished writer among the Arabian physicians of the Middle Ages.

Linacre's translations of Galen remain still the

standard, and they have been reprinted many times. As Erasmus once wrote to a friend, in sending some of these books of Galen, " I present you with the works of Galen, now by the help of Linacre speaking better Latin than they ever before spoke Greek." Linacre also translated Aristotle into Latin, and Erasmus paid them the high compliment of saying that Linacre's Latin was as lucid, as straightforward, and as thoroughly intelligible as was Aristotle's Greek. Of the translations of Aristotle unfortunately none is extant. Of Galen we have the " De Sanitate Tuenda," the " Methodus Medendi," the " De Symptomatum Differentiis et Causis," and the "De Pulsuum Usu." The latter particularly is a noteworthy monograph on an important subject, in which Galen's observations were of great value. Under the title, " The Significance of the Pulse," it has been translated into English, and has influenced many generations of English medical men.

While we have very few remains of Linacre's work as a physician, there seems to be no doubt that he was considered by all those best capable of judging, to stand at the head of his profession in England. To his care, as one of his biographers remarked, was committed the health of the foremost in Church and State. Besides being the Royal Physician, he was the regular medical attendant of Cardinal Wolsey, of Archbishop Warham, the Primate of England, of Richard Fox, Bishop of Winchester, the Keeper of the Privy Seal, and of Sir Reginald Bray, Knight of the Garter and Lord High Treasurer, and of all of the famous scholars of England.

Erasmus, whilst absent in France, writes to give him an account of his feelings, and begs him to prescribe for him, as he knows no one else to whom he can turn with equal confidence. After a voyage across the channel, during which he had been four days at sea—making a passage by the way that now takes less than two hours— Erasmus describes his condition, his headache, with the glands behind his ears swollen, his temples throbbing, a constant buzzing in his ears; and laments that no Linacre was at hand to restore him to health by skilful advice. In a subsequent letter he writes from Paris to ask for a copy of a prescription given him while in London by Linacre, but which a stupid servant had left at the apothecary shop, so that Erasmus could not have it filled in Paris.

An instance of his skill in prognosis, the most difficult part of the practice of medicine according to Hippocrates and all subsequent authorities, is cited by all his biographers, with regard to his friend William Lily, the grammarian. Lily was suffering from a malignant tumor involving the hip, which surgeons in consultation had decided should be removed. Linacre plainly foretold that its removal would surely prove fatal, and the event verified his unfavorable prognosis. Generally it seems to have been considered that his opinion was of great value in all serious matters, and it was eagerly sought for. Some of the nobility and clergy of the time came even from the Continent over to England—by no means an easy journey, even for a healthy man in those days, as can be appreciated from Erasmus's experience just cited—in order to obtain Linacre's opinion.

One of Erasmus's letters to Billibaldus Pirckheimer contains a particular account of the method of treatment by which he was relieved of his severe pain under Linacre's direction in a very tormenting attack of renal colic. The details, especially the use of poultice applications as hot as could be borne, show that Linacre thoroughly understood the use of heat in the relaxation of spasm, while his careful preparation of the remedies to be employed in the presence of the patient himself would seem to show that he had a very high appreciation of how much the mental state of the patient and the attitude of expectancy thus awakened may have in giving relief even in cases of severe pain.

The only medical writings of Linacre's that we possess are translations. We have said already that the reversion at the end of the fifteenth century to the classical authorities in medicine undoubtedly did much to introduce the observant phase of medical science, which had its highest expression in Vesalius at the beginning of the sixteenth century and continued to flourish so fruitfully during the next two centuries at most of the Italian universities. His translations then

were of themselves more suggestive contributions
to medicine than would perhaps have been any
even of his original observations, since the mind
of his generation was not ready as yet to be influenced by discoveries made by contemporaries.

The best proof of Linacre's great practical interest in medicine is his realization of the need
for the Royal College of Physicians and his
arrangements for it.

The Roll of the College, which comprises biographical sketches of all the eminent physicians
whose names are recorded in the annals from
the foundation of the College in 1518, and is
published under the authority of the College
itself, contains the best tribute to Linacre's work
that can possibly be paid. It says: " The most
magnificent of Linacre's labors was the design
of the Royal College of Physicians of London—
a standing monument of the enlightened views
and generosity of its projectors. In the execu-
tion of it Linacre stood alone, for the munificence
of the Crown was limited to a grant of letters
patent; whilst the expenses and provision of the
College was left to be defrayed out of his own
means, or of those who were associated with him
in its foundation." " In the year 1518," says
Dr. Johnson,[1] " when Linacre's scheme was carried into effect, the practice of medicine was
scarcely elevated above that of the mechanical
arts, nor was the majority of its practitioners

[1] " Life of Linacre," London, 1835.

among the laity better instructed than the mechanics by whom these arts were exercised. With the diffusion of learning to the republics and states of Italy, establishments solely for the advancement of science had been formed with success; but no society devoted to the interests of learning yet existed in England, unfettered by a union with the hierarchy, or exempted from the rigors and seclusions which were imposed upon its members as the necessary obligation of a monastic and religious life. In reflecting on the advantages which had been derived from these institutions, Linacre did not forget the impossibility of adapting rules and regulations which accorded with the state of society in the Middle Ages to the improved state of learning in his own, and his plans were avowedly modelled on some similar community of which many cities of Italy afforded rather striking examples."

Some idea of the state into which the practice of medicine had fallen in England before Linacre's foundation of the Royal College of Physicians may be gathered from the words of the charter of the College. "Before this period a great multitude of ignorant persons, of whom the greater part had no insight into physic, nor into any other kind of learning—some could not even read the letters on the book, so far forth that common artificers as smiths, weavers and women—boldly and accustomably took upon them great cures to the high displeasure of God, great infamy to the faculty, and the grievous hurt, damage, and destruction of many of the King's liege people."

After the foundation of the College there was a definite way of deciding formally who were, or were not, legally licensed to practise. As a consequence, when serious malpractice came to public notice, those without a license were occasionally treated in the most summary manner. Stowe, in his chronicles, gives a very vivid and picturesque description of the treatment of one of these quacks who had been especially flagrant in his imposition upon the people. A counterfeit doctor was set on horseback, his face to the horse's tail, the tail being forced into his hand as a bridle, a collar of jordans about his neck, a whetstone on his breast, and so led through the city of London with ringing of basins, and banished. "Such deceivers," continued the old chronicler, "no doubt are many, who being never trained up in reading or practice of physics and Chirurgery do boast to do great cures, especially upon women, as to make them straight that before were crooked, corbed, or crumped in any part of their bodies and other such things. But the contrary is true. For some have received gold when they have better deserved the whetstone." [1] Human nature has not changed very much in the

[1] "To get the whetstone" is an old English expression, meaning to take the prize for lying. It is derived from the old custom of driving rogues, whose wits were too sharp, out of town with a whetstone around their necks.

four centuries since Linacre's foundation, and
while the model that he set in the matter of pro-
viding a proper licensing body for physicians has
done something to lessen the evils complained of,
the abuses still remain; and the old chronicler
will find in our time not a few who, in his
opinion, might deserve the whetstone. We can
scarcely realize how much Linacre accomplished
by means of the Royal College of Physicians, or
how great was the organizing spirit of the man
to enable him to recognize the best way out of
the chaos of medical practice in his time.

" The wisdom of Linacre's plan," wrote Dr.
Friend, " speaks for itself. His scheme, without doubt, was not only to create a good understanding and unanimity among his own profession (which of itself was an excellent thought),
but to make them more useful to the public.
And he imagined that by separating them from
the vulgar empirics and setting them upon such
a reputable foot of distinction, there would always arise a spirit of emulation among men liberally educated, which would animate them in pursuing their inquiries into the nature of diseases
and the methods of cure for the benefit of mankind; and perhaps no founder ever had the good
fortune to have his designs succeed more to his
wish."

His plans with regard to the teaching of medicine at the two great English Universities did
not succeed so well, but that was the fault not of
Linacre nor of the directions left in his will, but

of the times, which were awry for educational matters. Notwithstanding Linacre's bequest of funds for two professorships at Oxford and one at Cambridge, it is typical of the times that the chairs were not founded for many years. During Henry VIII's time, the great effort of government was not to encourage new foundations but to break up old ones, in order to obtain money for the royal treasury, so that educational institutions of all kinds suffered eclipse. The first formal action with regard to the Linacre bequest was taken in the third year of Edward VI. Two lectureships were established in Merton College, Oxford, and one in St. John's College, Cambridge. Linacre's idea had been that these foundations should be University lectureships, but Anthony Wood says that the University had lost in prestige so much during Henry VIII's time that it was considered preferable to attach the lectureships to Merton College, which had considerable reputation because of its medical school. During Elizabeth's time these Linacre lectureships sank to be sinecures and for nearly a hundred years served but for the support of a fellowship. The Oxford foundation was revived in 1856 by the University Commissioners, and the present splendid foundation of the lectures in physiology bears Linacre's name in honor of his original grant.

At the age of about fifty Linacre was ordained priest. His idea in becoming a clergyman, as confessed in letters to his friends, was partly in

order to obtain leisure for his favorite studies,
but also out of the desire to give himself up to
something other than the mere worldly pursuits
in which he had been occupied during all his previous life. His biographer, Dr. Johnson, says:
" In examining the motives of this choice of
Linacre's, it would seem that he was guided less
by the expectation of dignity and preferment
than by the desire of retirement and of rendering
himself acquainted with those writings which
might afford him consolation in old age and relief from the infirmities which a life of assiduous
study and application had tended to produce."

The precise time of Linacre's ordination is not
known, nor is it certain whether he was ordained
by Archbishop Warham of Canterbury, or by
Cardinal Wolsey, the Archbishop of York. He
received his first clerical appointment from Warham, by whom he was collated to the rectory of
Mersham in Kent. He held this place scarcely
a month, but his resignation was followed by his
installation as prebend in the Cathedral of Wells,
and by an admission to the Church of Hawkhurst
in Kent, which he held until the year of his death.
Seven years later he was made prebend in the
Collegiate Chapel of St. Stephen, Westminster,
and in the following year he became prebendary
of South Newbold in the Church of York. This
was in the year 1518. In the following year he
received the dignified and lucrative appointment
of presentor to the Cathedral of York, for which
he was indebted to Cardinal Wolsey, to whom

about this time he dedicated his translation of
Galen " On the Use of the Pulse."   He seems
also to have held several other benefices during
the later years of his life, although some of them
were resigned within so short a time as to make
it difficult to understand why he should have
accepted them, since the expenses of institution
must have exceeded the profits which were derived from them during the period of possession.

Linacre owed his clerical opportunities during
the last years of his life particularly to Archbishop Warham, who, as ambassador, primate,
and chancellor, occupied a large and honorable
place in the history of the times.   Erasmus says
of him in one of his letters: " Such were his
vigilance and attention in all matters relating to
religion and to the offices of the Church that no
concern which was foreign to them seemed ever
to distract him.   He had sufficient time for a
scrupulous performance of the accustomed exercises of prayer, for the almost daily celebration
of the Mass, for twice or thrice hearing divine
service, for determining suits, for receiving em-
bassies, for consultation with the king when
matters of moment required his presence, for
the visitation of churches when regulation was
needed, for the welcome of frequently two hundred guests, and lastly for a literary leisure."

As the close friend of such men, it is evident
that Linacre must have accomplished much good
as a clergyman; and it seems not unlikely that
his frequent changes of rectorship were rather

due to the fact that the Primate wished to make
use of his influence in various parts of his diocese for the benefit of religion than for any personal motives on Linacre's part, who, in order
to enter the service of the Church, had given up
so much more than he could expect as a clergyman.

Linacre as a clergyman continued to deserve
the goodwill and esteem of all his former friends,
and seems to have made many new ones. At the
time of his death he was one of the most honored
individuals in England. All of his biographers
are agreed in stating that he was the representative Englishman of his time, looked up to by all
his contemporaries, respected and admired by
those who had not the opportunity of his intimate acquaintance, and heartily loved by friends,
who were themselves some of the best men of
the time.

The concluding paragraph of the appreciation
of Linacre's character in "Lives of British
Physicians" [1] is as follows: "To sum up his
character it was said of him that no Englishman
of his day had had such famous masters, namely,
Demetrius and Politian of Florence; such noble
patrons, Lorenzo de' Medici, Henry VII and
Henry VIII; such high-born scholars, the Prince
Arthur and Princess Mary of England; or such
learned friends, for amongst the latter were to
be enumerated Erasmus, Melanchthon, Latimer,

[1] London: John Murray, 1830.

Tonstal, and Sir Thomas More." His biographer might have added the names of others of the pre-Reformation period, men of culture and character whose merits only the historical researches of recent years have brought out—Prior Selling, Dean Colet (though his friendship was unfortunately interrupted), Archbishop Warham, Cardinal Wolsey, Grocyn, and further scholars and churchmen.

Dr. J. F. Payne, in summing up the opinion of Linacre held by his contemporaries, in the " Dictionary of National Biography " (British), pays a high tribute to the man. " Linacre's personal character was highly esteemed by his contemporaries. He was evidently capable of absolute devotion to a great cause, animated by genuine public spirit and a boundless zeal for learning." Erasmus sketches him humorously in the " Encomium Moriae " (The Praise of Foolishness)—with a play on the word *Moriae* in reference to his great friend, Thomas More, of whom Erasmus thought so much—showing him a tireless student. The distinguished foreign scholar, however, considered Linacre as an enthusiast in recondite studies, but no mere pedant. Dr. Payne closes his appreciation with these words: " Linacre had, it would seem, no enemies."

Caius, the distinguished English physician and scholar, himself one of the best known members of the Royal College of Physicians and the founder of Caius College, Cambridge, sketches

Linacre's character (he had as a young man known him personally) in very sympathetic vein. As Dr. Caius was one of the greatest Englishmen of his time in the middle of the sixteenth century, his opinion must carry great weight. It is to him that we owe the famous epitaph that for long in old St. Paul's, London, was to be read on Linacre's tombstone:—

"**Fraudes dolosque mire perosus, fidus amicis, omnibus ordinibus juxta carus—A** stern hater of deceit and underhand ways, faithful to his friends, equally dear to all classes."

Surely this is a worthy tribute to the great physician, clergyman, scholar, and philanthropist of the eve of the Reformation in England.

V.

FATHER KIRCHER, S.J.: SCIENTIST, ORIENTALIST, AND COLLECTOR.

OPORTET autem neque recenti-
ores viros in his fraudare quae
vel repere runt vel recte secuti sunt;
et tamen ea quae apud antiquiores
aliquos posita sunt auctoribus suis
reddere.—CELSUS *de Medicina*.

ATHANASIUS KIRCHER

V.

FATHER KIRCHER, S.J.: SCIENTIST, ORIENTALIST, AND COLLECTOR.

EXCEPT in the minds of the unconquerably intolerant, the Galileo controversy has in recent years settled down to occupy something of its proper place in the history of the supposed conflict between religion and science. In touching the subject in the life of Copernicus we suggested that it has come to be generally recognized, as M. Bertrand, the perpetual Secretary of the Paris Academy of Sciences, himself a distinguished mathematician and historian, declares, that "the great lesson for those who would wish to oppose reason with violence was clearly to be read in Galileo's story, and the scandal of his condemnation was learned without any profound sorrow to Galileo himself; and his long life, considered as a whole, was the most serene and enviable in the history of science." Somehow, notation, there is left still in the minds of many ation, there is still left in the minds of many an impression rather difficult to eradicate that there was definite, persistent opposition to everything associated with scientific progress among the churchmen of the time of Galileo.

Perhaps no better answer to this unfortunate, because absolutely untrue, impression could be formulated than is to be found in a sketch of the career of Father Athanasius Kircher, the distinguished Jesuit who for so many years occupied himself with nearly every branch of science in Rome, under the fostering care of the Church. He had been Professor of Physics, Mathematics, and Oriental Languages at Würzburg, but was driven from there by the disturbances incident to the Thirty Years' War, in 1631. He continued his scientific investigation at Avignon. From here, within two years after Galileo's trial in 1635, he was, through the influence of Cardinal Barberini, summoned to Rome, where he devoted himself to mathematics at first, and then to every branch of science, as well as the Oriental languages, not only with the approval, but also with the most liberal pecuniary aid from the ecclesiastical authorities of the papal court and city.

Some idea of the breadth of Father Kircher's scientific sympathy and his genius for scientific observation and discovery, which amounted almost to intuition, may be gathered from the fact that to him we owe the first definite statement of the germ theory of disease; and he seems to have been the first to recognize the presence of what are now called microbes. At the same time his works on magnetism contained not only all the knowledge of his own time, but also some wonderful suggestions as to the possibilities of the development of this science. His studies with regard to light are almost as epochal as those with regard to magnetism. Besides these, he was the first to find any clue to the Egyptian hieroglyphics, and yet found time to write a geographical work on Latium, the country surrounding Rome, and to make collections for his museum which rendered it in its time the best scientific collection in the world. It may very well indeed be said that visitors to Rome with scientific tendencies found as much that was suggestive in Father Kircher's museum—the "Kircherianum," as it came to be called—as artists and sculptors and architects found in the Vatican collections of the papal city.

All of this work was accomplished within the half century after Galileo's trial, for Father Kircher died in 1680, at the age of seventy-eight, having lived, as so many of the great scientists have done, a long life in the midst of the most persistent activity. Kircher, more than perhaps any other, can be said to be the founder of modern natural science. Before any one else, in a practical way, he realized the necessity for the collection of an immense amount of data, if science was to be founded on the broad, firm foundation of observed truth. The principle which had been announced by Bacon in the "Novum Organon"—"to take all that comes rather than to choose, and to heap up rather than to register"—was never carried out as fully as by Father Kircher. As Edmund Gosse said in the June number of "Harper's," 1904, "Bacon had started a great idea, but he had not carried it out. He is not the founder, he is the prophet of modern physical science. To be in direct touch with nature, to adventure in the unexplored fields of knowledge, and to do this by carrying out an endless course of slow and sure experiments, this was the counsel of the ' Novum Organon.' " Bacon died in 1626, and scarcely more than a decade had passed before Kircher was carrying out the work thus outlined by the English philosopher in a way that was surprisingly successful, even looked at from the standpoint of our modern science. Needless to say, however, it was not because of Bacon's suggestion that he did so, for it is more than doubtful whether he knew of Bacon's writings until long after the lines of his life-work had been traced by his own inquiring spirit. The fulness of time had come. The inductive philosophy was in the air. Bacon's formulæ, which the English philosopher never practically applied, and Father Kircher's assiduous collection of data, were but expressions of the spirit of the times. How faithfully the work of the first modern inductive scientist was accomplished we shall see.

It may be easily imagined that a certain interest in Father Kircher, apart from his scientific attainments and the desire to show how much and how successful was the attention given to natural science by churchmen about the time of the Galileo controversy, might influence this judgment of the distinguished Jesuit's scientific accomplishments. With regard to his discoveries in medicine especially, and above all his announce-

ment of the microbic origin of contagious disease,
it may be thought that this was a mere chance
expression and not at all the result of serious
scientific conclusions. Tyndall, however, the distinguished English physicist, would not be the
one to give credit for scientific discoveries, and
to a clergyman in a distant century, unless there
was definite evidence of the discovery. It is not
generally known that to the great English physicist we owe the almost absolute demonstration of
the impossibility of spontaneous generation, together with a series of studies showing the existence everywhere in the atmosphere of minute
forms of life to which fermentative changes and
also the infectious diseases—though at that time
this was only a probability—are to be attributed.
When Tyndall was reviewing, in the midst of the
controversy over spontaneous generation, the
question of the microbic origin of disease, he
said: " Side by side with many other theories has
run the germ theory of epidemic disease. The
notion was expressed by Kircher and favored by
Linnæus, that epidemic diseases may be due to
germs which enter the body and produce disturbance by the development within the body of
parasitic forms of life."

How much attention Father Kircher's book on
the pest or plague, in which his theory of the
micro-organismal origin of disease is put for-
ward, attracted from the medical profession can
be understood from the fact that it was submitted
to three of the most distinguished physicians in

Rome before being printed, and that their testimony to its value as a contribution to medicine prefaced the first edition. They are not sparing in their praise of it. Dr. Joseph Benedict Sinibaldus, who was the Professor of the Practice of Medicine in the Roman University at the time, says that " Father Kircher's book not only contains an excellent résumé of all that is known about the pest or plague, but also as many valuable hints and suggestions on the origin and spread of the disease, which had never before been made." He considers it a very wonderful thing that a non-medical man should have been able to place himself so thoroughly in touch with the present state of medicine in respect to this disease and then point out the conditions of future progress.

Dr. Paul Zachias, who was a distinguished Roman physician of the time, said that he had long known Father Kircher as an eminent writer on other subjects, but that after reading his book on the pest he must consider him also distinguished in medical writing. He says: " While he has set his hand at other's harvests, he has done it with so much wisdom and prudence as to win the admiration of the harvesters already in the field." He adds that there can be no doubt that it would be a source of profit for medical men to read this little book and that it will undoubtedly prove beneficial to future generations.

Testimony of another kind to the value of Father Kircher's book is to be found in the fact

that within a half-year after its publication in
Latin it appeared in several other languages.   It
is too much the custom of these modern times to
consider that scientific progress in the centuries
before our own and its immediate predecessor
was likely to attract little attention for many
years, and was especially slow to make its way
into foreign countries.   Anything, however, of
real importance in science took but a very short
time to travel from one country to another in
Europe in the seventeenth century, and the fact
that scientific men generally used Latin as a common language made the spread of discoveries and
speculations much easier even than at the present
time.   Our increased means of communication
have really only served to allow sensational announcements of a progress in science—which is
usually no progress at all—to be spread quite as
effectually in modern times as were real advances
in the older days.

There is no good account of Father Kircher's
life available in English, and it has seemed only
proper that the more important at least of the
details of the life of the man who thus anticipated
the beginnings of modern bacteriology and of the
relations of micro-organisms to disease, should
not be left in obscurity.   His life history is all the
more interesting and important because it illus-
trates the interest of the churchmen of the time,
and especially of the Roman ecclesiastical authorities, in all forms of science; for Father Kircher
is undoubtedly one of the greatest scholars of his-

tory and one of the scientific geniuses in whose works can be found, as the result of some wonderful principles of intuition incomprehensible to the slower intellectual operations of ordinary men, anticipations of many of the discoveries of the after-time. There is scarcely a modern science he did not touch upon, and nothing that he touched did he fail to illuminate. His magnificent collections in the museum of the Roman College demonstrate very well his extremely wide interests in all scientific matters.

The history of Father Kircher's career furnishes perhaps the best possible refutation of the oft-repeated slander that Jesuit education was narrow and was so founded upon and rooted in authority that original research and investigation, in scientific matters particularly, were impossible, and that it utterly failed to encourage new discoveries of any kind. As a matter of fact, Kircher was not only not hampered in his work by his superiors or by the ecclesiastical authorities, but the respect in which he was held at Rome enabled him to use the influence of the Church and of great churchmen all over the world, with the best possible effect, for the assembling at the Roman College of objects of the most various kinds, illustrating especially the modern sciences of archeology, ethnology, and paleontology, besides Egyptian and Assyrian history.

Athanasius Kircher was born 2 May, 1602, at Geisa, near Fulda, in South Germany. He was educated at the Jesuit College of Fulda, and at the early age of sixteen, having completed his college course, entered the Jesuit novitiate at Mainz. After his novitiate he continued his philosophical and classical studies at Paderborn and completed his years of scholastic teaching in various cities of South Germany—Munster, Cologne, and Coblenz—finally finishing his education by theological studies at Cologne and Mainz.

Toward the end of the third decade of the seventeenth century he became Professor of Philosophy and Mathematics at Würzburg. Here his interest in Oriental languages began, and he established a special course in this subject at the University of Würzburg. During the Thirty Years' War, however, the invasion of Germany very seriously disturbed university work, and finally in 1631 Father Kircher was sent by his superiors to Avignon in South France, where he continued his teaching some four years, attracting no little attention by his wide interest in many sciences and by various scientific works that showed him to be a man of very broad genius.

In 1635, through the influence of Cardinal Barberini, he was summoned to Rome, where he became Professor of Mathematics and Oriental Languages in the famous Roman College of the Jesuits, which was considered at that time one of the greatest educational institutions in the world. His interest in science, however, was not lessened by teaching duties that would apparently have demanded all his time; and, as we shall see, he continued to issue books on the most diverse scientific subjects, most of them illustrated by absolutely new experimental observations and all of them attracting widespread attention.

Father Kircher began his career as a writer on science at the early age of twenty-seven, when he issued his first work on magnetism. The title of this volume, "Ars Magnesia tum Theorematice tum Problematice Proposita," shows that the subject was not treated entirely from a speculative standpoint. Indeed, in the preface he states that he hopes that the principal value of the book will be found in the fact that the knowledge of magnetism is presented by a new method, with special demonstrations, and that the conclusions are confirmed by various practical uses and long-continued experience with magnets of various kinds.

Although it may be a source of great surprise, Father Kircher's genius was essentially experimental. He has been spoken of not infrequently as a man who collected the scientific information of his time in such a way as to display, as says the "Encyclopædia Britannica," "a wide and varied learning, but that he was a man singularly devoid of judgment and critical discernment." He was in some respects the direct opposite of the opinion thus expressed, since his learning was always of a practical character, and there are very few subjects in this writing which he has not himself illustrated by means of new and ingenious experiments.

Perhaps the best possible proof of this is to be

found in the fact that his second scientific work was on the construction of sun-dials, and that one of the discoveries he himself considered most valuable was the invention of a calculating machine, as well as of a complicated arrangement for illustrating the positions of the stars in the heavens. He constructed, moreover, a large burning-glass in order to demonstrate the possibility of the story told of Archimedes, that he had succeeded in burning the enemy's ships in the harbor at Syracuse by means of a large lens.

But Father Kircher's surest claim to being a practical genius is to be found in his invention of the magic lantern. It was another Jesuit, Aquilonius, in his work on optics, issued in 1613, who had first sought to explain how the two pictures presented to the two eyes are fused into one, and it was in a practical demonstration of this by means of lenses that Kircher hit upon the invention of the projecting stereoscope.

After his call to Rome our subject continued his work on magnetism, and in 1641 issued a further treatise on the subject called " Magnes " or " De Arte Magnetica." While he continued to teach Oriental languages and issued in 1644 a book with the title " Lingua Ægyptiaca Restituta," he also continued to apply himself especially to the development of physical science. Accordingly in 1645 there appeared his volume "Ars Magna Lucis et Umbrae." This was a treatise on light, illustrated, as was his treatise on magnetism, by many original experiments and demonstrations.

During the five years until 1650 the department of acoustics came under his consideration,
so that in that year we have from his pen a treatise called "Musurgia Universalis," with the sub-
title, "The Art of Harmony and Discord; a
treatise on the whole doctrine of sound with the
philosophy of music treated from the standpoint
of practical as well as theoretic science." During the next five years astronomy was his special
hobby, and the result was in 1656 a treatise on
astronomy called "Iter Celeste." This contained
a description of the earth and the heavens and
discussed the nature of the fixed and moving
stars, with various considerations as to the composition and structure of these bodies. A second
volume on this subject appeared in 1660.

The variety of Father Kircher's interests in
science was not yet exhausted, however. Five
years after the completion of his two volumes on
astronomy there came one on "Mundus Subter-
raneus." This treated of the modern subjects of
geology, metallurgy, and mineralogy, as well as
the chemistry of minerals. It also contained a
treatise on animals that live under the ground,
and on insects. This was considered one of the
author's greatest books, and the whole of it
was translated into French, whilst abstracts from
it, especially the chapters on poisons, appeared in
most of the other languages of Europe. Part of
it was translated even into English, though seven-
teenth-century Englishmen were loath to draw
their inspiration from Jesuit writers.

Jesuits were, however, at this time generally acknowledged on the Continent to be leaders in every department of thought, sympathetic coadjutors in every step in scientific progress. Strange as it may appear to those who will not understand the Jesuit spirit of love for learning, two of the most distinguished scientists whose names are immortal in the history of physical sciences in diffent departments during this century, Kepler and Harvey, were on intimate terms of friendship with the Jesuits of Germany. Harvey, on the occasion of a visit to the Continent, stopped for a prolonged visit with the Jesuits at Cologne, so that some of his English friends joked him about the possibility of his making converts of the Jesuits. These witticisms, however, did not seem to distract Harvey very much, for he returned on a subsequent occasion to spend some further days with his Jesuit scientific friends along the Rhine.

In the meantime Father Kircher was issuing notable books on his always favorite subject of the Oriental languages. In 1650 there appeared " Obeliscus Pamphilius," containing an explanation of the hieroglyphics to be found on the obelisk which by the order of Innocent X, a member of the Pamfili family, was placed in the Piazza Navona by Bernini. This is no mere pamphlet, as might be thought, but a book of 560 pages. In 1652 there appeared " Œdipus Ægyptiacus," that is, the revealer of the sphinx-like riddle of the Egyptian ancient languages. In 1653 a second volume of this appeared, and in 1655 a third

volume. It was considered so important that it
was translated into Russian and other Slav languages, besides several other European languages. His book, "Lingua Ægyptiaca Restituta," which appeared in 1644, when Kircher was
forty-two years of age, is considered to be of
value yet in the study of Oriental languages, and
was dedicated to the patron, Emperor Ferdinand
III, whose liberality made its publication possible.

It is often a subject for conjecture just how
science was studied and taught in centuries before the nineteenth, and just what text-books
were employed. A little familiarity with Father
Kircher's publications, however, will show that
there was plenty of very suitable material for
text-books to be found in his works. Under his
own direction, what at the present time would be
called a text-book of physics, but which at that
time was called "Physiologia Experimentalis,"
was issued, containing all the experimental and
demonstrative parts of his various books on chemistry, physics, music, magnetism, and mechanics,
as well as acoustics and optics. This formed the
groundwork of most text-books of science for a
full century afterwards. Indeed, until the beginning of the distinctly modern science of chemistry with the discoveries of Priestley and Lavoisier, there was to be little added of serious im-
port in science.

Perhaps the most commendable feature of
Father Kircher's books is the fact that he himself seems never to have considered that he had

exhausted a subject. The first work he published was on magnetism. Some twelve years later he returned to the subject, and wrote a more extensive work, containing many improvements over the first volume. The same thing is true of his studies in sound. In 1650, when not quite fifty years of age, he issued his " Musurgia Universalis," a sub-title of which stated that it contains the whole doctrine of sound and the practical and theoretical philosophy of music. A little over twenty years later, however, he published the "Phonurgia Nova," the sub-title of which showed that it was mainly concerned with the experimental demonstration of various truths in acoustics and with the development of the doctrine he had originally stated in the " Musurgia."

It is no wonder that his contemporaries spoke of him as the *Doctor centum artium*—the teacher of a hundred arts—for there was practically no branch of scientific knowledge in his time in which he was not expert. Scientific visitors to Rome always considered it one of the privileges of their stay in the papal city to have the opportunity to meet Father Kircher, and it was thought a very great honor to be shown through his museum by himself.

Of course, it is difficult for present-day scientists to imagine a man exhausting the whole round of science in this way. Many who have read but little more than the titles of Father Kircher's many books are accordingly prone to speak of him as a mine of information, but without any proper critical judgment. He has succeeded, according to them, in heaping together an immense amount of information, but it is of the most disparate value. There is no doubt that he took account of many things in science that are manifestly absurd. Astrology, for instance, had not, in his time, gone out of fashion entirely, and he refers many events in men's lives to the influence of the stars. He even made rules for astrological predictions, and his astronomical machine for exhibiting the motions of the stars was also meant to be helpful in the construction of astrological tables. It must not be forgotten, however, that in his time the best astronomers, like Tycho Brahe and even Kepler, had not entirely given up the idea of the influence of the stars over man's destiny.

As regards other sciences, there are details of information that may appear quite as superstitious as the belief in astrology. Kircher, for instance, accepted the idea of the possibility of the transmutation of metals. It is to be said, though, that all mankind were convinced of this possibility, and indeed not entirely without reason. All during the nineteenth century scientists believed very firmly in the absolute independence of chemical elements and their utter non-interchangeability. As the result of recent discoveries, however, in which one element has apparently been observed giving rise to another, much of this doctrine has come to be considered as improbable, and now the idea of possible transmutation of

metals and other chemical elements into one another appears not so absurd as it was half a century ago.

Any one who will take up a text-book of
science of a century ago will find in it many
glaring absurdities.   It will seem almost impossible that a scientific thinker, in his right senses,
could have accepted some of the propositions that
are calmly set down as absolute truths.   Every
generation has made itself ridiculous by knowing
many things " that are not so," and even ours is
no exception.   Father Kircher was not outside
this rule, though he was ahead of his generation
in the critical faculty that enabled him to elim-
inate many falsities and to illuminate half-truths
in the science of his day.

Undoubtedly the most interesting of Father
Kircher's scientific books is his work On the Pest,
with some considerations on its origin, mode of
distribution, and treatment, which about the
middle of the seventeenth century gathered together all the medical theories of the times as to
the causation of contagious disease, discussed
them with critical judgment and reached conclusions which anticipate much of what is most modern in our present-day medicine.   It is this work
of Father Kircher's that is now most often referred to, and very deservedly so, because it is
one of the classics which represents a landmark
in knowledge for all time.   It merits a place
beside such books as Harvey on the Circulation
of the Blood, or even Vesalius on Human Anat-

omy. As we have seen, it is now quoted from by our best recent authorities who attempt seriously to trace the history of the microbic theory of disease, and its conclusions are the result of logical processes and not the mere chance lighting upon truth of a mind that had the theories of the time before it. In it Father Kircher's genius is best exhibited. It has the faults of his too ready credibility; and his desire to discuss all possible phases of the question, even those which are now manifestly absurd, has led him into what prove to be useless digressions. But on the whole it represents very well the first great example of the application of the principle of inductive science to modern medicine. All the known facts and observations are collected and discussed, and then the conclusions are suggested.

It is very interesting to trace the development of Father Kircher's ideas with regard to the origin, causation, and communication of disease, because in many points he so clearly anticipates medical knowledge that has only come to be definitely accepted in very recent times. It has often been pointed out that Sir Robert Boyle declared that the processes of fermentation and those which brought about infectious disease, were probably of similar nature, and that the scientist who solved the problem of the cause of fermentation would throw great light on the origin of these diseases. This prophetic remark was absolutely verified when Pasteur, a chemist who had solved the problem of fermentation, also solved

the weightier questions connected with human
diseases.   Before even Boyle, however, Father
Kircher had expressed his opinion that disease
processes were similar to those of putrefaction.
He considered that putrefaction was due to the
presence of certain *corpuscula*, as he called them,
and these he said were also probably active in the
causation of infectious disease.

He was not sure whether or not these *corpuscula* were living, in the sense that they could
multiply of themselves.   He considered, however,
that this was very probable.   As to their distribution, he is especially happy in his anticipations
of modern medical progress.   While he considered it very possible that they were carried
through the air, he gives it as his deliberate
opinion that loving things were the most frequent
agents for the distribution of the corpuscles of
disease.   He is sure that they are carried by flies,
for instance, and that they may be inoculated by
the stings of such insects as fleas or mosquitoes.
He even gives some examples that he knew of in
which this was demonstrated.   Still more striking is his insistence on the fact that such a contagious disease as pest may be carried by cats and
dogs and other domestic animals.   The cat seemed
to him to be associated with special danger in this
matter, and he gives an example of a nunnery
which had carefully protected itself against possible infection, but had allowed a cat to come in,
with the result that some cases of the disease developed.

An interesting bit of discussion is to be found
in the chapter in which Father Kircher takes up
the consideration of the problem whether infectious disease can ever be produced by the imagination. He is speaking particularly of the pest,
but there is more than a suspicion that under the
name pest came at times of epidemics many of
our modern contagious diseases. Father Kircher
says that there is no doubt that worry plays an
important rôle in predisposing persons to take the
disease. He does not consider, however, that it
can originate of itself, or be engendered in the
person without contact with some previous case
of pest. With regard to the question of predis-
position he is very modern. He points out that
many persons do not take the disease, because
evidently of some protective quality which they
possess. He is sure, too, that the best possible
protection comes from keeping in good, general
health.

A curious suggestion is that with regard to the
grave-diggers and undertakers. It has often
been noted in Italy, so Father Kircher asserts,
that these individuals as a rule did not succumb to
the disease, notwithstanding their extreme expo-
sure, when the majority of the population were
suffering from it. Toward the end of the epidemic, however, at the time when the towns-
people were beginning to rejoice over its practical disappearance, it was not unusual to have
these caretakers of the dead brought down with
the disease—often, too, in fatal form. Father

Kircher considers that only strong and healthy individuals would take up such an occupation. That the satisfaction of accomplishing a large amount of work and making money kept them in good health. Later on, however, as the result of overwork during the time of the epidemic and also of discouragement because they saw the end of prosperous times for them, they became predisposed to the disease and then fell victims.

With regard to the prevention of the pest in individual cases, Father Kircher has some very sensible remarks. He says that physicians as a rule depend on certain medicinal protectives or on amulets which they carry. The amulets he considers to be merely superstitious. The sweet-smelling substances that are sometimes employed are probably without any preventive action. Certain physicians employed a prophylactic remedy made up of very many substances. This is what in modern days we would be apt to call a " gun-shot prescription." It contained so many ingredients that it was hoped that some one of them would hit the right spot and prove effective. Father Kircher has another name for it. We do not know whether it is original with him, but in any case it is worth while remembering. He calls it a " calendar prescription," because when written it resembled a list of the days of the month.

His opinion of this " calendar prescription " is not very high. It seems to him that if one ingredient did good, most of the others would be almost as sure to do harm. The main factor in prophylaxis to his mind was to keep in normal health, and this seemed not quite compatible with frequent recourse to a prescription containing so many drugs that were almost sure to have no good effect and might have an ill effect. It is all the more interesting to find these common-sense views because ordinarily Father Kircher is set down as one who accepted most of the traditions of his time without inquiring very deeply into their origin or truth, simply reporting them out of the fulness of his rather pedantic information. In most cases it will be found, however, that, like Herodotus, reporting the curious things that had been told him in his travels, he is very careful to state what are his own opinions and what he owes to others and gives place to, though without attaching much credence to them.

It must not be forgotten that his great contemporaries, Von Helmont and Paracelsus, were not free from many of the curious scientific superstitions of their time, though they had, like him, in many respects the true scientific spirit. Von Helmont, for instance, was a firm believer in the doctrine of spontaneous generation, and even went so far as to consider that it had its application to animals of rather high order. For instance, one of his works contains a rather famous prescription to bring about the spontaneous generation of mice. What was needed was a jar of meal kept in a dark corner covered by some soiled linen. After three weeks these elements would be found to have bred mice. Too much must not be expected, then, of Kircher in the matter of crediting supposedly scientific traditions.

It may seem surprising that Father Kircher's book did not produce a greater impression upon the medical research work and teaching of the day and lead to an earlier development of microbology. Unfortunately, however, the instruments of precision necessary for such a study were not then at hand, and the gradual loss of prestige of the book is therefore readily to be understood. The explanation of this delay in the development of science is very well put by Crookshank, who is the professor of comparative pathology and bacteriology at King's College, London, and one of the acknowledged authorities on these subjects in the medical world. Professor Crookshank says, at the beginning of the first chapter of his text-book on bacteriology, in which he traces the origin of the science, that the first attempt to demonstrate the existence of the *contagium vivum* dates back almost to the discovery of the microscope [1]:—

Athanasius Kircher nearly two and a half centuries ago expressed his belief that there were definite micro-organisms to which diseases were attributable. The microscope had revealed that all decomposing substances swarmed with countless micro-organisms which were in-

[1] "A Text-Book of Bacteriology." Including the Etiology and Prevention of Infectious Diseases. By Edgar M. Crookshank. Fourth Edition. London, 1896.

visible to the naked eye, and Kircher sought for similar
organisms in disease, which he considered might be due
to their agency. The microscopes which he describes
obviously could not admit of the possibility of studying
or even detecting the micro-organisms which are now
known to be associated with certain diseases ; and it is
not surprising that his teaching did not at the time gain
much attention. They were destined, however, to receive a great impetus from the discoveries which eman-
ated not long after from the father of microscopy,
Leeuwenhoek.

This reference to Kircher's work, however,
shows that more cordial appreciation of his scientific genius has come in our day, and it seems not
unlikely that in the progress of more accurate
and detailed knowledge of scientific origins his
reputation will grow as it deserves. With that
doubtless will come a better understanding of the
true attitude of the scholars of the time—so many
of whom were churchmen—to so-called physical
science in contradistinction to philosophy, in
which of course they had always been profoundly
interested. The work done by Kircher could
never have been accomplished but for the sympathetic interest of those who are falsely supposed to have been bitterly opposed to all progress in the natural sciences, but whose opposition
was really limited to theoretic phases of scientific inquiry that threatened, as has scientific
theory so often since, to prove directly contra-
dictory to revealed truth.

VI.

BISHOP STENSEN: ANATOMIST AND FATHER OF GEOLOGY.

GOD makes sages and saints that they may be fountain-heads of wisdom and virtue for all who yearn and aspire: and whoever has superior knowledge or ability is thereby committed to more effectual and unselfish service of his fellow-men. If the love of fame be but an infirmity of noble souls, the craving of professional reputation is but conceit and vanity. To be of help, and to be of help not merely to animals, but to immortal, pure, loving spirits—this is the noblest earthly fate.—BISHOP SPALDING: *The Physician's Calling and Education.*

NICOLAUS STENONIS

VI.

BISHOP STENSEN, ANATOMIST AND FATHER OF GEOLOGY.

IN the sketch of the life of Father Athanasius Kircher, the distinguished Jesuit scientist, mathematician, and Orientalist, I called attention to the fact that, at the very time when Galileo was tried and condemned at Rome, because of his abuse of Scripture for the demonstration of scientific thesis, a condemnation which has been often since proclaimed to be due to the Church's intolerant opposition to science, the ecclesiastical authorities at Rome invited Father Kircher, who was at that time teaching mathematics in Germany, to come to Rome, and during the next half-century encouraged him in every way in the cultivation of all the physical sciences of the times. It was to popes and cardinals, as well as to influential members of his own order of the Jesuits, that Father Kircher owed his opportunities for the foundation of a complete and magnificent museum, illustrating many phases of natural science—the first of its kind in the world, and which yet continues to be one of the noteworthy collections.

During the decade in which the condemnation of Galileo and the invitation of Father Kircher to Rome took place, there was born, at Copen-

138 CATHOLIC CHURCHMEN IN SCIENCE

hagen, a man whose career of distinction in science was to prove even more effectively than that of Kircher, if possible, that there was no opposition in ecclesiastical circles in Italy, during this century, to the development of natural science even in departments in respect to which the Church has, over and over again, been said to be specially intolerant. This scientist was Nicholas Stensen, the discoverer of the duct of the parotid gland, which conducts saliva into the mouth, and the founder, in the truest sense of the word, of the modern science of geology. Stensen's discovery of the duct which has since borne his name was due to no mere accident; for he was one of the really great anatomists of all time, and one distinguished particularly for his powers of original observation and investigation. To have the two distinctions, then, of a leader in anatomy and a founder in geology, stamps him as one of the supreme scientific geniuses of all time, a man not only of a fruitfully inquiring disposition of mind, but also one who possessed a very definite realization of how important for the cause of scientific truth is the necessity of testing all ideas with regard to things physical, by actual observations of nature and by drawing conclusions not wider than the observed facts.

Notwithstanding this characteristically scientific temper of mind, which, according to most modern ideas, at least, would seem to be sure to lead him away from religious truth, Stensen at the

very height of his career as a scientist, while
studying anatomy and geology in Italy, became
a convert from Lutheranism, in which he had
been born, to Catholicity, and thereafter made it
one of the prime objects of his life to bring as
many others as possible of the separated brethren into the fold of the Church. When he accepted the professorship of anatomy at the University of Copenhagen, it was with the definite
idea that he might be able to use the influence of
his position to make people realize how much of
religious truth there was in the old Church from
which they had been separated in the preceding
century. After a time, however, his zeal led him
to resign his position, and ask to be made a
priest, in order that he might be able more effectively to fulfil what he now considered the main
purpose of his life, the winning of souls to the
Church. As, since his conversion, he had given
every evidence of the most sincere piety and
humble simplicity, his desires were granted. His
book on geology, however, was partly written
during the very time when he was preparing for
sacred orders, and was warmly welcomed by all
his Catholic friends. After spending some time
as a missionary, and attracting a great deal of
attention by his devout life and by the many
friends and converts he succeeded in making, the
recently converted Duke of Hanover asked that
the zealous Danish convert should be made bishop
of his capital city. This request was immediately granted, and Stensen spent several years

in the hardest missionary labor in his new field. As a matter of fact, his labors proved too much for his rather delicate constitution, and he died at the comparatively early age of forty-eight. The visitor to the University of Copenhagen marvels to find among the portraits of her professors of anatomy one in the robes of a Roman Catholic bishop. This is Stensen. In 1881, when the International Geographical Congress met at Bologna, it adjourned at the end of the session to Florence to unveil a bust of Stensen, over his tomb there. Here evidently is a man whose life is well worth studying, because of all that it means for the history of his time.

Nicholas Stensen—or, as he is often called, Steno, because this is the Latin form of his name, and Latin was practically exclusively used, during his age, in scientific circles all over Europe— was born 20 January, 1638, in Copenhagen. His father died while he was comparatively young, and his mother married again, both her husbands being goldsmiths in high repute for their skill, and both of them in rather well-to-do circumstances. His early education was obtained at Copenhagen, and the results displayed in his attainments show how well it must have been conducted. Later in life he spoke and wrote Latin very fluently and had, besides, a very thorough knowledge of Greek and of Hebrew. Of the modern languages, German, French, Italian, and Low Dutch he knew very well, mainly from residence in the various countries in which they

are spoken. A more unusual attainment at that
time, and one showing the ardor of his thirst for
knowledge, was an acquaintance with English.
In early life he was especially fond of mathematics and, indeed, it was almost by accident that
this did not become his chosen field of educational development.

At eighteen he became a student of the University of Copenhagen, and after some preliminary studies in philosophy and philology devoted
himself mainly to medicine. At this time the
Danish University was especially distinguished
for its work in anatomy. The famous family of
Bartholini, who had for several generations been
teaching there, had proved a copious source of
inspiration for the students in their department,
and as a consequence original investigation of a
high order, with enthusiasm for the development
of anatomical science, had become the rule. The
external situation was not favorable to learning,
for Denmark was engaged in harassing and
costly wars during a considerable portion of the
seventeenth century; yet the work accomplished
here was, undoubtedly, some of the best in
Europe. Young Stensen had the advantage of
having Thomas Bartholini as his preceptor, and
soon, because of his enthusiasm for science, as
friend and father.

Stensen had been at the University scarcely
two years when the city of Copenhagen was be-
sieged by the Swedes. Professor Lutz, of the
University of St. Louis, who has recently written

an article on Stensen, which appeared in the
"Medical Library and Historical Journal" for
July, 1904, says of this period:—

A regiment of students numbering two hundred and
sixty-six, called "the black coats" on account of their
dark clothes, was formed for the defence of the city ;
upon its roster we find the name of young Steno.   During the day they were at work mending the ramparts,
and the nights were spent in repelling the attacks of the
enemy.   In the course of this long siege, the city was
compelled to cope with a more formidable enemy than
the Swedes—famine with all its horrors—before relief
came in the shape of provisions and reinforcements furnished by the Dutch fleet.   Throughout these turbulent
days the student soldiers rendered valuable services to
their country, and though it be true that "inter arma
silent musae"—"the war gods do not favor the muses"
—it appears nevertheless that Steno attended the lectures
and dissections which were conducted by the teachers in
the intervals when the students were not on duty.

After some three years spent at the University
of Copenhagen, Stensen, as was the custom of
the times, went to pursue his post-graduate
studies in a foreign university.   Bartholini furnished him with a letter of recommendation to
Professor Blasius, who was teaching anatomy at
Amsterdam in Holland.   Amsterdam had become famous during the seventeenth century for
the very practical character of its anatomical
teaching.   As the result of the cordial commen-
dation of Bartholini, Stensen became an inmate
of the house of Professor Blasius, and was given

special opportunities to pursue his anatomical studies for himself. He had been but a very short time at Amsterdam, when he made the discovery to which his name has ever since been attached, that of the duct of the parotid gland. Stensen's discovery was made while he was dissecting the head of a sheep. He found shortly afterwards, however, that the canal could be demonstrated to exist in the dog, though it was not so large a structure. Blasius seems to have been rather annoyed at the fact that a student, just beginning work with him, should make so important a discovery, and wished to claim the honor of it for himself. There is no doubt, however, now, notwithstanding the discussion over the priority of the discovery which took place at the time, that Stensen was the first to make this important observation.

Not long before, Wharton, an English observer, had demonstrated the existence of a canal leading from the submaxillary gland into the mouth. This might have been expected to lead to the discovery of other glandular ducts, but so far had not. As a matter of fact, the function of the parotid gland was not well understood at this time. During the discussion as to priority of discovery, Steno pointed out one fact which he very properly considers as the most conclusive proof that Blasius did not discover the duct of the gland. He says: " Blasius shows plainly in his treatise ' De Medicina Generali ' that he has never sought for the duct, for he does not assign

to it either the proper point of beginning or end-
ing, and assigns to the parotid gland itself so unworthy a function as that of furnishing warmth
to the ear, so that if I were not perfectly sure
of having once shown him the duct myself, I
should be tempted to say that he had never
seen it."

Bartholini settled the controversy, and at the
same time removed any discouragement that
might have arisen in his young pupil's mind, by
writing to him:—

Your assiduity in investigating the secrets of the human body, as well as your fortunate discoveries, are
highly praised by the learned of your country. The
fatherland congratulates itself upon such a citizen, I upon
such a pupil, through whose efforts anatomy makes daily
progress, and our lymphatic vessels are traced out more
and more. You divide honors with Wharton, since you
have added to his internal duct an external one, and
have thereby discovered the sources of the saliva concerning which many have hitherto dreamed much, but
which no one has (permit the expression) pointed out
with the finger. Continue, my Steno, to follow the path
to immortal glory which true anatomy holds out to you.

Under the stimulus of such encouragement, it
is no wonder that Stensen continued his original
work with eminent success. He published an extensive article on the glands of the eye and the
vessels of the nose.

Bartholini wrote to him again: "Your fame
is growing from day to day, for your pen and
your sharp eye know no rest." Later he wrote

again: " You may count upon the favor of the
king as well as upon the applause of the learned."
After three years at the University of Amsterdam, Steno returned to Copenhagen, where he
published his "Anatomical Observations Concerning the Muscles and Glands." It was in this
book that he announced his persuasion that the
heart was a muscle. As he said himself, " the
heart has been considered the seat of natural
warmth, the throne of the soul; but if you examine it more closely, it turns out to be nothing
but a muscle. The men of the past would not
have been so grossly mistaken with regard to it,
had they not preferred their imaginary theories
to the results of the simple observation of
nature." It is easy to understand that this observation created a very great sensation. It had
much to do with overthrowing certain theoretic
systems of medicine, and nearly a century later
the distinguished physiologist, Haller, did not
hesitate to proclaim the volume in which it occurs,
as a " golden book."

Stensen's studies in anatomy stamp him as an
original genius of a high order, and this is all
the more remarkable because his career occurs
just in those years when there were distinguished
discoverers in anatomy in every country in
Europe. When Stensen began his work in anatomy, Harvey was still alive. The elder Bartholini, the first who ever established an anatomical
museum, was another of his contemporaries.
Among the names of distinguished anatomists

with whom Stensen was brought intimately in contact during the course of his studies in Holland, France and Italy are those of Swammerdam, Van Horne, and Malpighi. There is no doubt that his intercourse with such men sharpened his own intellectual activity, and increased his enthusiasm for original investigation in contradistinction to the mere accumulation of information.

His contemporaries, indeed, exhausted most of the adjectives of the Latin language in trying to express their appreciation of his acuity of observation. He was spoken of as *oculatissimus*—that is, as being all eyes, *subtilissimus, acutissimus, sagacissimus* in his knowledge of the human body, and as the most perspicacious anatomist of the time. Leibnitz and Haller were in accord in considering him one of the greatest of anatomists. In later years this admiration for Stensen's genius has not been less enthusiastically expressed. Haeser, in his " History of Medicine," the third edition of which appeared at Jena in 1879, says: "Among the greatest anatomists of the seventeenth century belongs Nicholas Steno, the most distinguished pupil of Thomas Bartholini. Steno was rightly considered in his own time as one of the greatest of anatomical discoverers. There is scarcely any part of the human body the knowledge of which was not rendered more complete by his investigations."

The most valuable discovery made by Stensen was undoubtedly that the heart is a muscle. It must not be forgotten that in his time, Harvey's discovery of the circulation of the blood was not yet generally accepted; indeed, there were many who considered the theory (as they called it) of the English investigator as one of the passing fads of medicine. Two significant discoveries, made after Harvey, served, however, to establish the theory of the circulation of the blood on a firm basis and to make it a definite medical doctrine. The most important of these was Malpighi's discovery that the capillaries—that is, the minute vessels at the end of the arterial tree on the surface of the body and in various organs—served as the direct connexion between the veins and the arteries. This demonstrated just how the blood passed from the arterial to the venous system. Scarcely less important, however, for the confirmation of Harvey's teaching was Stensen's demonstration of the muscular character of the tissue of the heart.

Some of his observations upon muscles are extremely interesting, and, though he made many mistakes in explaining their function, he added not a little to the anatomical and physiological knowledge of the time in their regard. He seems to have been one of the first to recognize the fact that in the higher animals the heart may continue to beat for a considerable time after the animal is apparently dead; and, indeed, that by irritation of the removed heart, voluntary contractions may be brought about which will continue spontaneously for some moments.

With regard to the objections made by some, that such studies as these upon muscles could scarcely be expected to produce any direct result for the treatment of disease, or in the ordinary practice of medicine, Stensen said in reply that it is only on the basis of the anatomical, physiological, and pathological observation that progress in medicine is to be looked for.   In spite, then, of the discouragement of the many, who look always for immediate practical results, Stensen continued his investigation, and even proposed to make an extended study of the mechanism of the muscular action.

In the meantime, however, there had gradually been coming into his life another element which was to prove more absorbing than even his zeal for scientific discovery.   It is this which constitutes the essential index of the man's character and has been sadly misunderstood by many of his biographers.

Sir Michael Foster, of Cambridge, England, in his " Lectures on the History of Physiology," originally delivered as the Lane Lectures at Cooper Medical College, San Francisco, said :—

While thus engaged, still working at physiology, Stensen turned his versatile mind to other problems, as well as to those of comparative anatomy, and especially to those of the infant, indeed hardly as yet born, science of geology.   His work " De solido intra solidum " is thought by geologists to be a brilliant effort toward the beginning of their science.

In 1672 he returned for a while to his native city of

Copenhagen, but within two years he was back again at Florence ; and then there came to him, while as yet a young man of some thirty-six summers, a sudden and profound change in his life.

In his early days he had heard much, too much perhaps, of the doctrines of Luther. Probably he had been repelled by the austere devotion which ruled the paternal roof. And, as his answer to Bossuet shows, his university life and studies, his intercourse with the active intellects of many lands, and his passion for inquiry into natural knowledge, had freed him from passive obedience to dogma. He doubtless, as did many others of his time, looked upon himself as one of the enlightened, as one raised above the barren theological questions which were moving the minds of lesser men.

Yet it was out of this sceptical state of mind, that life in Italy and intimate contact with ecclesiastics and religious, so often said to be likely not to have any such effect, brought this acute scientific mind into the Catholic Church. Nor did he become merely a formal adherent, but an ardent believer, and then an enthusiastic proselytizer. One American writer of a history of medicine, in his utter failure to comprehend or sympathize with the change that came over Stensen, speaks of him as having become at the end of his life a mere " peripatetic converter of heretics." This phase of Stensen's life has, however, as ample significance as any that preceded it.

Steno's expectations of the professorship of anatomy at Copenhagen were disappointed, but the appointment went to Jacobson, whose work indeed is scarcely less distinguished than that of his unsuccessful rival. The next few years Stensen passed in Paris, where he was assiduous in making dissections, and where he attracted much attention; and then, somewhat later, in Italy; in 1665 and 1666 he was in Rome. Thence he went to Florence, in order to perfect himself in Italian. The next few years he spent in this city, having received the appointment of body physician to the Grand Duke, as well as an appointment of visiting physician, as we would call it now, to the Hospital of Santa Maria Nuova.

It was while at Florence that the whole current of Stensen's life was changed by his conversion to Catholicity. His position as physician to the Hospital of Santa Maria Nuova brought him frequently into the apothecary shop attached to the hospital. As a result he came to know very well the religious in charge of the department, Sister Maria Flavia, the daughter of a well-known Tuscan family. At this time she had been for some thirty-five years a nun. Before long she learned that the distinguished young physician, at this time scarcely thirty years of age, who was such a pleasant gentleman in all his ways, was a Lutheran. She began, as she told afterwards, first by prayer, and then by friendly suggestions, to attempt to win him to the Catholic Church. Stensen, who seems already to have been well-disposed toward the Church, and who had always been known for a wonderful purity of heart and simplicity of character, listened very willingly to the naive words of the old religious, who might very well have been his mother.

Many years later, by the command of her confessor, the good Sister related the detailed story of his conversion. She began very simply by telling him one day that if he did not accept the true Catholic faith, he would surely go to hell. He listened to this without any impatience, and she said it a number of other times, half jokingly perhaps, but much more than half in earnest. As he listened so kindly, she said to him one day that he must pray every day to God to let him know the truth. This he promised to do and, as she found out from his servant (what is it these nuns do not find out?) he did pray every evening. One day, while he was in the apothecary shop, the Angelus bell rang, and she asked him to say the Angelus. He was perfectly willing to say the first part of the Hail Mary, but he did not want to say the second part, as he did not believe in the invocation of the Blessed Virgin and the saints. Then she asked him to visit the Church of the Blessed Virgin, the Santissima Nunziata, which he did. After this she suggested to him that he should abstain from meat on Fridays and Saturdays, which he promised to do, and which the good nun found out once more from his servant, he actually did do. And then the religious thought it was time to suggest that he should consult a clergyman, and his conversion was not long delayed.

Young Stensen seems to have been the object

of solicitude on the part of a number of the good, elderly women with whom he was brought in contact. He discussed with Signora Arnolfini the great difficulty he had in believing the mystery of the Eucharist. Another good woman, the Signora Lavinia Felice, seeing how interested he was in things Catholic, succeeded in bringing him to the notice of a prominent Jesuit in Florence. As his friend, Sister Maria Flavia, had recommended the same Father to him, he followed the advice all the more readily, and it was not long before his last doubts were solved.

It was after his conversion that Stensen received his invitation to become the professor of anatomy at the University of Copenhagen. Much as he had become attached to Florence, the thought of returning to his native city was sweet; and then besides he hoped that he might be able to influence his countrymen in their views toward the Catholic Church. It was not long, however, before the bigotry of his compatriots made life so unpleasant for him in Copenhagen that he resigned his position and returned to Italy. Various official posts in Florence were open for him, but now he had resolved to devote himself to the service of the Church, and so he became a priest. His contemporary, the Cardinal Archbishop of Florence, said with regard to him: "Already as a member of a Protestant sect he had lived a life of innocence and had practised all the moral virtues. After his conversion he had marked out for himself so severe a method of life and had

remained so true to it that in a very short time
he reached a high degree of perfection." The
Archbishop does not hesitate to say that he had
become a man of constant union with God and
entirely dead to himself. There was very little
hesitation, then, in accepting him as a candidate
for the priesthood, and as his knowledge of theology was very thorough, most of the delay in
raising him to that dignity came from his own
humility and his desire to prepare himself properly for the privilege. He made the exercises of
St. Ignatius as part of his preparation, and after
his ordination it was a source of remark with
how much devotion he said his first and all succeeding Masses. It was not long before the
piety of Stensen's life attracted great attention.
At this time he was in frequent communication
with such men as Spinoza and Leibnitz, the distinguished philosophers. It is curious to think
of the ardent mystic, the pantheistic philosopher,
and the speculative scientist, so different in character, having many interests in common.

It was during these years in Italy that Stensen
did what must be considered, undoubtedly, his
most important work, even more important, if
possible, than his anatomical discoveries. This
was his foundation of the science of geology. As
has been well said in a prominent text-book of
geology, his book on this subject sets him in that
group of men who as prophets of science often
run far ahead of their times to point out the path
which later centuries will follow in the road of

knowledge. It is rather surprising to find that the seventeenth century must enjoy the privilege of being considered the cradle of geological knowledge. There is no doubt, however, that the great principles of the science were laid down in Stensen's little book, which he intended only to be an introduction to a more extensive work, but the latter was unfortunately never completed, nor, indeed, so far as we are able to decide now, ever seriously begun.

One of the basic principles of the science of geology Stensen taught as follows: "If a given body of definite form, produced according to the laws of nature, be carefully examined, it will show in itself the place and manner of its origin." This principle he showed would apply so comprehensively that the existence of many things, hitherto apparently inexplicable, became rather easy of solution. It must not be forgotten that before this time two explanations for the existence of peculiar bodies, or of ordinary bodies, in peculiar places, had been offered. According to one school of thought, the fossils found deep in the earth, or sometimes in the midst of rocks, had been created there. It was as if the creative force had run beyond the ordinary bounds of nature and had produced certain things, ordinarily associated with life, even in the midst of dead matter. The other explanation suggested was that the flood had in its work of destruction upon earth caused many anomalous displacements of living things, and had buried some of the animals under such circumstances that later they were found even beneath rocks, or deep down in the earth, far beyond where the animals could be supposed to have penetrated by any ordinary means during life.

Stensen had observed very faithfully the various strata that are to be found wherever special appearances of the earth's surface were exposed, or wherever deep excavations were made. His explanations of how these various strata are formed will serve to show, perhaps better than anything else, how far advanced he was in his realization of ideas that are supposed to belong only to modern geology. He said: " The powdery layers of the earth's surface must necessarily at some time have been held in suspension in water, from which they were precipitated by their own weight. The movement of the fluid scattered the precipitate here and there and gave to it a level surface."

" Bodies of considerable circumference," Stensen continues, " which are found in the various layers of the earth, followed the laws of gravity as regards their position and their relations to one another. The powdery material of the earth's strata took on so completely the form of the bodies which it surrounded that even the smallest apertures became filled up and the powdery layer fitted accurately to the surface of the object and even took something of its polish."

With regard to the composition of the various strata of the earth, the father of geology con-

sidered that if in a layer of rock all the portions
are of the same kind there is no reason to deny
that such a layer came into existence at the time
of creation, when the whole surface of the earth
was covered with fluid. If, however, in any one
stratum portions of another stratum are found,
or if the remains of plants or animals occur, there
is no doubt that such a stratum had not its origin
at the time of creation, but came into existence
later.

If there is to be found in a stratum traces of
sea salt, or the remains of sea animals, or portions of vessels, or such like objects, which are
only to be encountered at the bottom of the sea,
then it must be considered that this portion of
the earth's surface once was below the sea level,
though it may happen that this occurred only by
the accident of a flood of some kind. The great
distance from the sea, or other body of water, at
the present time, may be due to the sinking of
the water level in the neighborhood, or by the
rising up of a mountain from some internal terrestrial cause in the interval of time. He continues :—

If one finds in any layer remains of branches of trees,
or herbs, then it is only right to conclude that these objects were brought together because of flood or of some
such condition in the place where they are now found.
If in a layer coal and ashes and burnt clay or other
scorched bodies are found, then it seems sure that some
place in the neighborhood of a watercourse a fire took
place, and this is all the more sure when the whole layer

consists of ashes and coal.   Whenever in the same place
the material of which all the layers is composed is the
same, there seems to be no doubt that the fluid to which
the stratum owes its origin did not at different times
obtain different material for its building purposes.

In respect to the mountains and their formation, Stensen said very definitely :—

All the mountains which we see now have not existed
from the beginning of things.   Mountains do not, however, grow as do plants.   The stones of which mountains
are composed have only a certain analogy with the bones
of animals, but have no similarity in structure or in
origin, nor have they the same function and purpose.
Mountain ranges, or chains of mountains as some prefer
to call them, do not always run in certain directions,
though this has sometimes been claimed.   Such claims
correspond neither to reason nor to observation.   Mountains may be very much disturbed in the course of years.
Mountain peaks rise and fall somewhat.   Chasms open
and shut here and there in them, and though there are
those who pretend that it is only the credulous who will
accept the stories of such happenings, there is no doubt
that they have been established on trustworthy evidence.

In the course of his observations in Italy,
Stensen had seen many mussel shells, which had
been gathered from various layers of the earth's
surface.   With regard to the shells themselves,
he said that there could be no doubt that they
had come as the excretion of the mantle of the
mussel, and that the differences that could be
noted in them were in accordance with the varying forms of these animals.   He pointed out,
however, that some of the mussel shells found in

strata of rock were really mussel shells in every respect as regards the material of which they were composed as well as their interior structure and their external form, so that there could be no possible question of their origin. On the other hand, a certain number of the so-called mussel shells were not composed of the ordinary materials of which such shells are usually made up; but had indeed only the external form of genuine shells. Stensen considered, however, that even these must be regarded as originating in real mussel shells, the original substance having been later on replaced by other material. He explained this replacement process in very much the same way that we now suggest the explanation of various processes of petrification. There is no doubt that in this he went far beyond his contemporaries, and pointed out very clearly what was to be the teaching of generations long after his own.

The same principles he applied to mussel shells, Stensen considered must have their application also to all other portions of animal bodies, teeth, bones, whole skeletons, and even more perishable animal materials that might be found buried in the earth's strata. His treatment of the question of the remains of plants was quite as satisfactory as that of the animals. He distinguished between the impressions of plants, the petrification of plants, the carbonization of plants, and then dwelt somewhat on the tendency of certain minerals to form dendrites, that is, branching processes which look not unlike plants. He pointed out how easy it is to be deceived by these appearances, and stated very clearly the distinction between real plants and such simulated ones.

It will be scarcely necessary for us to apologize for having given so much space to Stensen's work on geology. Many distinguished scientists, however, have insisted that no greater advance at the birth of a science was ever made than that which Stensen accomplished in his geological work. Hoffman says that after carefully studying the work, he has come to the conclusion that of the successors of Stensen, no student of the mountains down to Werner's day had succeeded in comprehending so many fruitful points of view in geology. None of his great successors in geology has succeeded in introducing so many new ideas into the science as the first great observer. For several centuries most of his successors in geology remained far behind him in creative genius, and so there is little progress worth while noting in the knowledge of the method of earth formation, until almost the beginning of the nineteenth century, though his little book was written in 1668 and 1669.

Leibnitz regretted very much that Stensen did not complete his work on geology as he originally intended. Had he succeeded in gathering together all of his original observations, illustrated by the material he had collected, his work would have had much greater effect. As it was, the golden truth which he had expressed in such few words, without being able always to state just how he had come to his conclusions, was only of avail to science in a limited way. Men had to repeat his observations long years afterwards in order to realize the truth of what he had laid down. Leibnitz considered that it took more than a century for geological science to reach the point at which it had been left by Steno's work, and which he had reached at a single bound. There is scarcely a single modern geologist interested at all in the history of the science who has not paid a worthy tribute to Steno's great basic discoveries in the science. It was not a matter for surprise, then, that the International Congress of Geologists which met at Bologna in 1881 assembled at his tomb in Florence in order to do him honor, after the regular sessions of the Congress had closed. They erected to his memory a tablet with the following inscription: " Nicolae Stenonis imaginem vides hospes quam aere collato docti amplius mille ex universo terrarum orbe insculpendam curarunt in memoriam ejus diei IV cal. Octobr. an. MDCCCLXXXI quo geologi post conventum Bononiae habitum praeside Joanne Capellinio equite huc peregrinati sunt atque adstantibus legatis flor Municipii et R. Instituti Altiorum doctrinarum cineres viri inter geologos et anatomicos praestantissimi in hujus templi hypogaeo laurea corona honoris gratique animi ergo honestaverunt." [1]

[1] You behold here, traveller, the bust of Nicholas Steno, as it

Stensen's work brought him in contact with
some of the distinguished men of the seventeenth
century, all of whom learned to appreciate his
breadth of intelligence and acuity of judgment.
We have already mentioned his epistolary relation with Spinoza, and have said something about
the controversy with Leibnitz, into which, in spite
of his disinclination to controversy generally, he
was drawn by the circumstances of the time and
the solicitation of friends. Another great thinker
of the century with whom he was brought into
intimate relationship was Des Cartes, the distinguished philosopher. In fact, Des Cartes's system of thought influenced Stensen not a little,
and he felt, when describing the function of
muscles in the human body, and especially when
he demonstrated that the heart was a muscle, that
the mechanical notions he was thus introducing
into anatomy were likely to prove confirmatory
of Des Cartes's philosophic speculations. Almost
more than any other, Stensen was the father of
many ideas that have since become common, with
regard to the physics of the human body and its
qualities as a machine.

With his breadth of view, from familiarity

was set up by more than a thousand scientists from all over the
world, as a memorial to him, on the fourth of the Kalends of
October, 1881. The geologists of the world, after their meeting
in Bologna, under the presidency of Count John Capellini, made
a pilgrimage to his tomb, and in the presence of the chosen rep-
presentatives of the municipality, and of the learned professors
of the University, honored the mortal ashes of this man, illustrious among geologists and anatomists.

with the progress of science generally in his time, Steno's discussions of the reason for the lack of exact knowledge and for the prevalence of error, in spite of enthusiastic investigation, are worth while appreciating. He considered that the reason why so many portions of natural science are still in doubt is that in the investigation of natural objects no careful distinction is made between what is known to a certainty and what is known only with a certain amount of assurance. He discusses the question of deductive and inductive science, and considers that even those who depend on experience will not infrequently be found in error, because their conclusions are wider than their premises, and because it only too often happens that they admit principles as true for which they have no sure evidence. Stensen considered it important, therefore, not to hurry on in the explanation of things, but, so far as possible, to cling to old-time principles that had been universally accepted, since nearly always these would be found to contain fruitful germs of truth.

He was universally acknowledged as one of the greatest original thinkers of his time, and his conversion to the Church did much to dissipate religious prejudices among those of German nationality. His influence over distinguished visitors who came to Florence, and who were very glad to have the opportunity of making his acquaintance, was such that not a few Northern visitors became, like himself, converts to the Church.

It was in the midst of this that the request of
the Duke of Hanover came that he should consent to become the bishop of his capital city. It
was only after Stensen had been put under holy
obedience that he would consent to accept the
proffered dignity. His first thought was to dis-
tribute all his goods among the poor, and betake
himself even without shoes on his feet, on a
pedestrian journey to Rome. First, however, he
made a pilgrimage to Loretto, where he arrived
so overcome by the fatigue of the journey that
the clergyman who took care of him while there,
insisted on his accepting a pair of shoes from
him, though he could not prevail upon him to
travel in any other way than on foot.

His first action, after his consecration as
bishop, was to write a letter, sending his episcopal benediction to Sister Maria Flavia, to whom
he felt he owed the great privilege of his life.
His lasting sense of satisfaction and consolation
in his change of religion may be appreciated from
what is, perhaps, the most interesting personal
document that we have from Stensen's own hand,
in which, on the eighteenth anniversary of his
conversion, he writes to a friend to describe his
feelings. " To-morrow," he says, " I shall finish,
God willing, the eighteenth year of my happy life
as a member of the Church. I wish to acknowledge once more my thankfulness for the part
which you took under God in my conversion.
As I hope to have the grace to be grateful to Him
forever, so I sigh for the opportunity to express

my thankfulness to you and your family. I can feel that my own ingratitude toward God, my slowness in His service, make me unworthy of His graces; but I hope that you who have helped me to enter his service will not cease to pray, so that I may obtain pardon for the past and grace for the future, in order in some measure to repay all the favors that have been conferred on me."

The distinguishing characteristic of his life as a bishop was his insistence on poverty as the principal element of his existence. He refused to enter his diocese in state in the carriage which the Duke offered to provide for him, but proceeded there on foot. No question of supposed dignity could make him employ a number of servants, and his only retainers were converts made by himself, who helped in the household and whom he treated quite as equals. He became engaged in one controversy on religious matters, but said that he did not consider that converts had ever been made by controversies. He compared it, indeed, to the gladiatorial contests in which the contestants had their heads completely enveloped in armor, so as to prevent any possible penetration of the weapons of an opponent. He insisted especially that in religious controversies the contending parties do not realize the significance given to words by each other, and that therefore no good can result.

After a time, Stensen did not find his work in Hamburg very satisfactory, because it was typically a missionary country, and the Jesuit missionaries who had been introduced were accomplishing all that could be hoped for. Accordingly, when the Duke of Mecklenburg-Schwerin became a convert to the Catholic Church, and asked that Stensen should be sent as a bishop into his dukedom, the request was complied with. Here, in the hardest kind of labor as a missionary, and in the midst of poverty that was truly apostolic, Stensen worked out the remaining years of his life. At his death he was looked upon as almost a saint. Notwithstanding his close relationship with two reigning princes, he did not leave enough personal effects to defray the expenses of his funeral. Besides his bishop's ring, and the very simple episcopal cross he wore, he had nothing of any value except some relics of St. Francis Xavier, St. Ignatius Loyola, and St. Philip Neri, which he had prized above all other treasures.

His missionary labors had not been marked by any very striking success in the number of converts made. In this his life would seem to have been a bitter personal disappointment. He never looked upon it as such, however, but continued to be eminently cheerful and friendly until the end. As a matter of fact, the influence of his career was to be felt much more two centuries after his death than during his lifetime. At the present moment, his life is well known in northern Germany, thanks to the biographic sketch written by Father Plenkers for the " Stimmen aus Maria Laach," which has been very widely circulated since its appearance in 1884. Something of the reaction among scientific minds in Germany toward a healthier orthodoxy of feeling, with regard to great religious questions, is undoubtedly due to the spread of the knowledge of the career of the great anatomist and geologist who gave up his scientific work for the sake of the spread of the higher truth.

After his death the Medici family asked for and obtained the privilege of having his body buried in San Lorenzo at Florence, with the members of the princely Medici house. More and more do visitors realize that the tablet over his remains chronicles the death of a man who was undoubtedly one of the world's great scientists, and one of the most original thinkers of his time, and that time a period greatly fertile in the history of science.

VII.

ABBE HAÜY, FATHER OF CRYS-
TALLOGRAPHY.

THEY continue this day as they were created, perfect in number and measure and weight, and from the ineffaceable characters impressed on them we may learn that those aspirations after accuracy in measurement, truth in statement, and justice in action, which we reckon among our noblest attributes as men, are ours because they are essential constituents of the image of Him who in the beginning created not only heaven and earth, but the materials of which heaven and earth consist.— CLERK MAXWELL *On the Molecule,* "Nature," Vol. VIII. 1873.

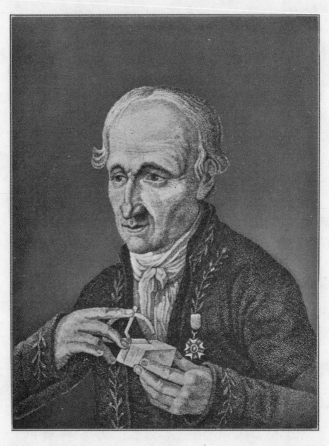

RÉNÉ   JUST   HAÜY

VII.

ABBÉ HAÜY,[1] FATHER OF CRYSTALLOGRAPHY

MODERN learning is gradually losing something of the self-complacency that characterized it in so constantly harboring the
thought that the most important discoveries in
physical science came in the nineteenth century.
A more general attention to critical history has
led to the realization that many of the primal
discoveries whose importance made the development of modern science possible, came in earlier
centuries, though their full significance was not
then fully appreciated. The foundations of most
of our modern sciences were, indeed, laid in the
eighteenth century, but some of them came much
earlier. It is genius alone that is able to break
away from established traditions of knowledge,
and, stepping across the boundary into the unknown, blaze a path along which it will be easy
for subsequent workers to follow. Only in recent years has the due meed of appreciation for
these great pioneers become part of the precious
traditions of scientific knowledge.

We have seen that clergymen were great original investigators in science in the older times
and we shall find, though it may be a source of

[1] Pronounced ä-üe (Century Dictionary), nearly represented
by *ah-we.*

169

astonishment to most people that even our modern science has had some supreme original workers, during the last two centuries, in the ranks of the Catholic clergy.

The eighteenth century was not behind the seventeenth in original contributions made to science by clergymen. About the middle of the century, a Premonstratensian monk, Procopius Dirwisch by name, of the little town of Prenditz in Bohemia, demonstrated the identity of electrical phenomena with lightning, thus anticipating the work of our own Franklin. Dirwisch dared to set up a lightning-conductor, by which during thunderstorms he obtained sparks from clouds, and also learned to appreciate the danger involved in this experiment. When, in 1751, he printed his article on this subject, he pointed out this danger. His warning, however, was not always heeded, and at least one subsequent experimenter was struck dead by a charge of electricity.

Just at the junction of the last two centuries, Father Piazzi enriched the realm of science by one of the most important of modern discoveries in astronomy. On the night of 31 December, 1800—1 January, 1801, he discovered the little planet Ceres. This was the first of the asteroids, so many more of which were to be revealed to astronomical study during the next half-century. Father Piazzi's discovery was made, not by accident, but as the result of detailed astronomical work of the most painstaking character. He had set out to make a map of the heavens, and to determine and locate the absolute position of all the visible stars. He had succeeded in cataloguing over 7,000 stars when his attention was called to one, hitherto supposed to be fixed, which he found had moved, during the interval between two observations, from its original position. He made still other observations, and thus determined the fact that it was a planetoid and not a fixed star with which he had to deal. Needless to say, his discovery proved a strong incentive to patient astronomical study of the same kind; and it is to these, rather than to great single discoveries, that we owe whatever progress in astronomy was made during the nineteenth century.

Contemporary with both of these last-mentioned men, and worthy to share in the scientific honors that were theirs, was the Abbé Haüy, who toward the end of the second half of the eighteenth century founded the science of crystallography; made a series of observations the value of which can never be disputed, originated theories some of which have served down to our own time as the basis of crystal knowledge, and attracted the attention of many students to the new science because of his charming personal character and his winning teaching methods. His life is a typical example of the value of work done in patient obscurity, founded on observation, and not on brilliant theories; and what he accomplished stamps him as one of the great scientific geniuses of all time—one of the men who widened the bounds of knowledge in directions hitherto considered inaccessible to the ordinary methods of human investigation.

It is a commonplace of the lecturer on popular science at the present day, that the impulse to the development of our modern scientific discoveries which became so marked toward the end of the eighteenth century, was due in a noteworthy degree to the work of the French Encyclopedists. Their bringing together of all the details of knowledge in a form in which it could be readily consulted, and in which previous progress and the special lines of advance could be realized, might be expected to prove a fruitful source of suggestive investigation. As a matter of fact, however, a detailed knowledge of the past in science often seems to be rather a hindrance than a help to original genius, always prone to take its own way if not too much disturbed by the conventional knowledge already gained. Most of the great discoverers in science were comparatively young men when they began their careers as original investigators; and it was apparently their freedom from the incubus of too copious information that left their minds untrammelled to follow their own bent in seeking for causes where others had failed to find any hints of possible developments.

This was certainly the case with regard to many of those distinguished founders who lived in centuries prior to the nineteenth. Most of

them were men under thirty years of age, and
not one of them had been noted, before he began
his own researches, for the extent of his knowledge in the particular department of science in
which his work was to prove so fruitful. Their
lives illustrate the essential difference there is
between theory and observation in science. The
theorizer reaches conclusions that are popular as
a rule in his own generation, and receives the
honor due to a progressive scientist; the observer
usually has his announcements of what he has
actually seen scouted by those who are engaged
in the same studies, and it is only succeeding
generations who appreciate how much he really
accomplished.

This was especially exemplified in the case of
the Abbé Haüy, whose work in crystallography
was to mean so much. What he learned was not
from books, but from contact with the actual objects of his department of science; and it is because the example of a life like this can scarcely
fail to serve a good purpose for the twentieth-
century student, in impressing the lesson of the
value of observation as opposed to theory, that
its details are retold.

René Just Haüy was born 28 February, 1743,
in the little village of Saint-Just, in the Department of Oise, somewhat north of the center of
France. Like many another great genius, he
was the son of very poor parents. His father
was a struggling linen-weaver, who was able to
support himself only with difficulty. At first

there seemed to be no other prospect for his eldest son than to succeed to his father's business. Certainly there seemed to be no possibility that he should be able to gain his livelihood by any other means than by the work of his hands.

Fortunately, however, there was in Haüy's native town a Premonstratensian monastery, and it was not long before some of the monks began to notice that the son of the weaver was of an especially pious disposition and attended church ceremonies very faithfully. The chance was given to him to attend the monastery school, and he succeeded admirably in his studies. As a consequence, the prior had his attention directed to the boy, and found in him the signs of a superior intelligence. He summoned the lad's parents and discussed with them the possibility of obtaining for their son an education. There were many difficulties in the way, but the principal one was their absolute financial inability to help him. If the son was to obtain an education, it must be somehow through his own efforts, and without any expense to his parents.

The prior thereupon obtained for young Haüy a position as a member of a church choir in Paris; and, later, some of those to whom he had recommended the boy secured for him a place in the college of Navarre. Here, during the course of a few years, he made such an impression upon the members of the faculty that they asked him to become one of the teaching corps of the institution. It was a very modest position that he held, and his salary scarcely more than paid for his board and clothes and a few books. Haüy was well satisfied, however, because his position provided him with opportunities for pursuing the studies for which he cared most. At this time he was interested mainly in literature, and succeeded in learning several languages, which were to be of considerable use to him later on in his scientific career.

After some years spent in the college of Navarre he was ordained priest, and not long afterward became a member of the faculty of the college of Cardinal Lemoine. Here his position was somewhat better, and he was brought in contact with many of the prominent scholars of Paris. He seems, however, to have been quite contented in his rather narrow circle of interests, and was not specially anxious to advance himself. It is rather curious to realize that a man who was later to spend all his time in the pursuit of the physical sciences, knew practically nothing at all about them, and certainly had no special interest in any particular branch of science, until he reached the age of almost thirty years.

Even then his first introduction to serious science did not come because of any special interest that had been aroused in his own mind, but entirely because of his friendship for a distinguished old fellow-professor, whose walks he used to share, and who was deeply interested in botany. This was the Abbé Lhomond, a very well known scholar, to whom we owe a number of classic text-books arranged especially for young folk.

The Abbé's recreation consisted in botanizing expeditions; and Haüy, who had chosen the kindly old priest as his spiritual director, was his most frequent companion. Occasionally, when M. Lhomond was ailing, and unable to take his usual walks, Haüy spent the time with him. He rather regretted the fact that he did not know enough about botany to be able to make collections of certain plants to bring to the professor at such times, in order that the latter might not entirely miss his favorite recreation. Accordingly, one summer when he was on his vacation at his country home, he asked one of the Premonstratensian monks, who was very much interested in botany, to teach him the principles of the science, so as to enable him to recognize various plants. Of course his request was granted. He expected to have a pleasant surprise for Abbé Lhomond on his return, and to draw even closer in his friendly relations with him, because of their mutual interest in what the old Abbé called his *scientia amabilis* (lovely science). His little plan worked to perfection, and there was won for the study of physical science a new recruit, who was to do as much as probably any one of his generation to extend scientific knowledge in one department, though that department was rather distant from botany.

Haüy's interest in botany, however, was to

prove only temporary. It brought him in contact with other departments of natural history, and it was not long before he found that his favorite study was that of minerals, and especially of the various forms of crystals. So absorbed did he become in this subject that nothing pleased him better than the opportunity to spend long days in the investigation of the comparative size and shape of the crystals in the museum at Paris. A friend has said of him that, whether they were the most precious stones and gems or the most worthless specimens of ordinary minerals, it was always only their crystalline shape that interested Haüy. Diamonds he studied, but only in order to determine their angles; and apparently they had no more attraction for him than any other well-defined crystal—much less, indeed, than some of the more complex crystalline varieties, which attracted his interest because of the difficulty of the problems they presented.

Like many another advance in science, Haüy's first great original step in crystallography was the result of what would be called a lucky accident. These accidents, however, be it noted, happen only to geniuses who are capable of taking advantage of them. How many a man had seen an apple fall from a tree before this little circumstance gave Newton the hint from which grew, eventually, the laws of gravity! Many a man, doubtless, had seen little boys tapping on logs of wood, to hear how well sound was carried through a solid body, without getting from this any hint, such as Laennec derived from it, for the invention of the stethoscope. So, too, many a person before Haüy's time had seen a crystal fall and break, leaving a smooth surface, without deriving any hint for the explanation of the origin of crystals.

According to the familiar story, Haüy was one day looking over a collection of very fine crystals in the house of Citizen Du Croisset, Treasurer of France. He was examining an especially fine specimen of calcspar, when it fell from his hands and was broken. Of course the visitor was much disturbed by this accident. His friend, however, in order to show him that he was not at all put out at the breaking of the crystal, insisted on Haüy's taking it with him for purposes of study, as they had both been very much interested in the perfectly smooth plane of the fracture. As Haüy himself says, this broken portion had a peculiarly brilliant lustre, "polished, as it were by nature," as beautifully as the outer portions of the crystal; thus demonstrating that in building up of so large a crystal there must have been certain steps of progress, at any of which, were the formation arrested, smooth surfaces would be found.

On taking the crystal home, Haüy proceeded further to break up the smaller fragment; and he soon found that he could remove slice after slice of it, until there was no trace of the original prism, but in place of it a rhomboid, perfectly similar to Iceland spar, and lying in the middle of what was the original prism. This fact seemed to him very important. From it he began the development of a theory of crystallization, using this observation as the key. Before this time it had been hard for students of mineralogy to understand how it was that substances of the same composition might yet have what seemed to be different crystalline forms. Calcspar, for instance, might be found crystallized in forms, apparently, quite at variance with one another.

By his studies, however, Haüy was able to determine that whenever substances of the same composition crystallized, even though the external form of the crystals seemed to be different, all of them were found to have the same internal nucleus. Whenever the mineral under observation was chemically different from another, then the nucleus also had a distinctive character; and so there came the law that all substances of the same kind crystallized in the same way, notwithstanding apparent differences. Indeed, one of the first results of this law was the recognition of the fact that when the crystalline forms of two minerals were essentially different, then, no matter how similar they might be, there was sure to be some chemical difference. This enabled Haüy to make certain prophecies with regard to the composition of minerals.

A number of different kinds of crystals had been classed together under the name of heavyspar. Some of these could not, by the splitting process, be made to produce *nuclei* of similar forms, and the angles of the crystals were quite different. Haüy insisted that, in spite of close resemblances, there was an essential distinction in the chemical composition of these two different crystalline formations; and before long careful investigation showed that, while many of the specimens called heavyspar contain barium, some of them contain a new substance—strontium— which had been very little studied heretofore. This principle did not prove to be absolute in its application; but the amount of truth in it attracted attention to the subject of crystallography because of the help which that science would afford in the easy recognition of the general chemical composition of mineral substances.

The most important part of Haüy's work was the annunciation of the law of symmetry. He emphasized the fact that the forms of crystals are not irregular or capricious, but are very constant and definite, and founded on absolutely fixed and ascertainable laws. He even showed that, while from certain crystalline *nuclei* sundry secondary forms may be derived, there are other forms that cannot by any possibility occur. Any change of crystalline form noticed in his experiments led to a corresponding change along all similar parts of the crystal. The angles, the edges, the faces, were modified in the same way, at the same time. All these elements of mensuration within the crystal Haüy thought could be indicated by rational coefficients.

Crystallography, however, did not absorb all Haüy's attention. He further demonstrated his intellectual power by following out other important lines of investigation that had been suggested by his study of crystals. It is to him more than to any other, for instance, that is due the first steps in our knowledge of pyro- (or thermo-) electricity. Mr. George Chrystal, professor of mathematics at the University of St. Andrews in the article on electricity written for the ninth edition of the Encyclopedia, says it was reserved for the Abbé Haüy in his Treatise on Mineralogy to throw a clear light on this curious branch of the science of electricity.

To those who are familiar with the history of the development of this science it will be no surprise to find a clergyman playing a prominent rôle in its development. During the days of the beginning of electricity many ecclesiastics seem to have been particularly interested in the curious ways of electrical phenomena, and as a consequence they are the original discoverers of some of the most important early advances. Not long before this, Professor Gordon, a Scotch Benedictine monk who was teaching at the University of Erfurt, constructed the first practical electrical machine. Kleist, who is one of the three men to whom is attributed the discovery of the principle of storing and concentrating electricity, and who invented the Leyden Jar, which was named after the town where it was first manufactured, was also a member of a Religious Order. As

we have already stated, Dirwisch, the Premonstratensian monk, set up a lightning-conductor
by which he obtained sparks from the clouds even
before our own Franklin.

Abbé Haüy was only following a very common precedent, then, when he succeeded by his
original research in setting the science of pyroelectricity firmly on its feet. It is true, others
before him had noted that substances like tourmaline possessed electrical properties. There is
even some good reason for thinking that the
lyncurium of the ancients which, according to
certain of the Greek philosophers, especially The-
ophrastus, who seems to have made a close study
of the subject, attracted light bodies, was really
our modern tourmaline. In modern times the
Dutch found this mineral in Ceylon and, because
it attracted ashes and other light substances to
itself, called it *aschentriker*—that is, attractor of
ashes. Others had still further experimented
with this curious substance and its interesting
electrical phenomena. It remained for Abbé
Haüy, however, to demonstrate the scientific
properties of tourmaline and the relations which
its electrical phenomena bore toward the crystalline structure of the mineral. He showed that
the electricity of tourmaline decreases rapidly
from the summits or poles toward the middle of
the crystal. As a matter of fact, at the middle
of the crystal its electrical power becomes im-
perceptible.

He showed also that each particle of a crystal

that exhibits pyroelectricity is itself a source of the same sort of electricity and exhibits polarity. His experimental observations served to prove also that the pyroelectric state has an important connexion with the want of symmetry in the crystals of the substances that exhibit this curious property. In tourmaline, for instance, he found the vitreous charge always at the summit of the crystal which had six faces, and the resinous electricity at the summit of the crystal with three faces.

His experiments soon showed him, too, that there were a number of other substances, besides tourmaline, which possessed this same electrical property when subjected to heat in the crystalline stage. Among these were the Siberian and Brazilian topaz, borate of magnesia, mesotype, sphene, and calamine. In all of these other pyroelectrical crystals, Haüy detected a corresponding deviation from the rules of symmetry in their secondary crystals to that which occurs in tourmaline. In a word, after he had concluded his experiments and observations there was very little left for others to add to this branch of science, although such distinguished men as Sir David Brewster in England were among his successors in the study of the peculiar phenomena of pyroelectricity.

It may naturally enough be thought that, born in the country, of poor parents, and compelled to work for his living, Haüy would at least have the advantage of rugged health to help him in his career. He had been a delicate child, however; and his physical condition never improved to such an extent as to inure him to hardships of any kind. One of his biographers has gone so far as to say that his life was one long malady. The only distraction from his almost constant suffering was his studies. Yet this man lived to be nearly eighty years of age, and accomplished an amount of work that might well be envied even by the hardiest.

In the midst of his magnificent success as a scientist, Haüy was faithful to all his obligations as a priest. His name was known throughout Europe, and many of the scientific societies had considered that they were honoring themselves by conferring titles, or degrees, upon him; but he continued to be the humble, simple student that he had always been.

At the beginning of the Revolution, Abbé Haüy was among the priests who refused the oath which the Republican government insisted on their taking, and which so many of them considered derogatory to their duty as churchmen. Those who refused were thrown into prison, Haüy among them. He did not seem to mind his incarceration much, but he was not a little perturbed by the fact that the officers who made the arrest insisted on taking his precious papers, and that his crystals were all tossed aside and many of them broken. For some time he was kept in confinement with a number of other members of the faculty of the University, mainly clergymen, in the Seminary of St. Firmin, which had been turned into a temporary jail.

Haüy did not allow his studies to be entirely interrupted by his imprisonment. He succeeded in obtaining permission to have his cabinets of crystals brought to his cell, and he continued his investigation of them. It was not long before powerful friends, and especially his scientific colleague, Gregory St. Hilaire, interested themselves in his case, and succeeded in obtaining his liberation. When the order for his release came, however, Haüy was engaged on a very interesting problem in crystallography, and he refused to interrupt his work and leave the prison. It was only after considerable persuasion that he consented to go the next morning. It may be added that only two weeks later many from this same prison were sent to the guillotine.

It is rather remarkable that the Revolutionary government, after his release, did not disturb him in any way. He was so much occupied with his scientific pursuits that he seems to have been considered absolutely incapable of antagonizing the government; and, as he had no enemies, he was not denounced to the Convention. This was fortunate, because it enabled him to pursue his studies in peace. There was many another member of the faculty of the University who had not the same good fortune. Lavoisier was thrown into prison, and, in spite of all the influence that could be brought to bear, the great discoverer of oxygen met his death by the guillotine. At least two others of the professors in the physical department, Borda and De Lambre, were dismissed from their posts. Haüy, though himself a priest who had refused to take the oath, and though he continued to exercise his religious functions, did not hesitate to formulate petitions for his imprisoned scientific friends; yet, because of his well-known gentleness of character, this did not result in arousing the enmity of any members of the government, or attracting such odious attention as might have made his religious and scientific work extremely difficult or even prevented it entirely.

Notwithstanding the stormy times of the French Revolution and the stirring events going on all round him in Paris, Haüy continued to study his crystals in order to complete his observations; and then he embodied his investigations and his theories in his famous "Treatise on Crystallography." This attracted attention not only on account of the evident novelty of the subject, but more especially because of the very thorough method with which Haüy had accomplished his work. His style, says the historian of crystallography, was "perspicuous and elegant. The volume itself was noteworthy for its clear arrangement and full illustration by figures." In spite of its deficiencies, then—deficiencies which must exist in any ground-breaking work—this monograph has had an enduring influence. Some of the most serious flaws in his theory were soon brought to light because of the very stimulus afforded by his investigations.

As to the real value of his treatise, perhaps no better estimate can be formed than that given by Cuvier in his collection of historical eulogies (Vol. III, p. 155): "In possession of a large collection, to which there flowed from all sides the most varied minerals, arranged with the assistance of young, enthusiastic, and progressive students, it was not long before there was given back to Haüy the time which he had apparently wasted over other things. In a few years he raised up a wondrous monument, which brought as much glory to France as it did somewhat later to himself. After centuries of neglect, his country at one bound found itself in the first rank in this department of natural science. In Haüy's book are united in the highest degree two qualities which are seldom associated. One of these is that it was founded on an original discovery which had sprung entirely from the genius of its author; and the other is that this discovery is pursued and developed with almost unheard-of persistence down even to the least important mineral variety. Everything in the work is great, both as regards conception and detail. It is as complete as the theory it announces."

It was not surprising, then, that, after the death of Professor Dolomieu, Haüy should be raised to the chair of mineralogy and made director of that department in the Paris Museum of Natural History. Here he was to have new triumphs. We have already said that his book was noted for the elegance of its style and its perspicuity.

As the result of this absolute clearness of ideas, and completeness and simplicity of expression, Haüy attracted to him a large number of pupils. Moreover, all those interested in the science, when they came in contact with him, were so charmed by his grace and simplicity of manner that they were very glad to attend his lectures and to be considered as his personal friends. Among his listeners were often such men as La Place, Berthollet, Fourcroy, Lagrange and Lavoisier.

It was not long before honors of all kinds, degrees from universities and memberships in scientific societies all over Europe, began to be heaped upon Haüy. They did not, however, cause any change in the manners or mode of life of the simple professor of old times. Every day he continued to take his little walks through the city, and was very glad to have opportunity to be of assistance to others. He showed strangers the way to points of interest for which they inquired, whenever it was necessary, obtained entrance cards for them to the collection; and not a few of those who were thus enabled to take advantage of his kindness failed to realize who the distinguished man was to whom they owed their opportunities. His old-fashioned clothing still continued to be quite good enough for him, and his modest demeanor and simple speech did not betray in any way the distinguished scientist he had become.

Some idea of the consideration in which the

Abbe Haüy was held by his contemporaries may be gathered from the fact that several of the reigning monarchs of Europe, as well as the heirs apparent to many thrones, came at some time or other to visit him, to see his collection, and to hear the kindly old man talk on his hobby. There was only one other scientist in the nineteenth century—and that was Pasteur, toward the end of it—who attracted as much attention from royalty. Among Haüy's visitors were the King of Prussia, the Emperor of Austria, the Archduke John, as well as the Emperor of Russia and his two brothers, Nicholas and Michael, the first of whom succeeded his elder brother, Alexander, to the throne, and half a century later was ruling Russia during the Crimean War. The Prince Royal of Denmark spent a portion of each year for several years with Haüy, being one of his intimates, who was admitted to his room while he was confined to his bed, and who was permitted to share his personal investigations and scientific studies.

His most striking characteristic was his suavity toward all. The humblest of his students was as sure to receive a kindly reception from him, and to have his difficulties solved with as much patience, as the most distinguished professor in this department. It was said that he had students of all classes. The attendants at the normal school were invited to visit him at his house, and he permitted them to learn all his secrets. When they came to him for a whole day, he insisted on taking part in their games, and allowed them to go home only after they had taken supper with him.   All of them looked upon him as a personal friend, and some of them were more confidential with him than with their nearest relatives.   Many a young man in Paris during the troublous times of the Revolutionary period found in the good Abbé Haüy not only a kind friend, but a wise director and another father.

It is said that one day, when taking his usual walk, he came upon two former soldiers who were just preparing to fight a duel and were on their way to the dueling ground.   He succeeded in getting them to tell him the cause of their quarrel, and after a time tempted them to come with him into what I fear we should call at the present day a saloon.   Here, over a glass of wine, he finally persuaded them to make peace and seal it effectually.   It is hard to reconcile this absolute simplicity of character and kindness of heart with what is sometimes assumed to be the typical, distant, abstracted, self-centered ways of the great scientist.

Few men have had so many proofs of the lofty appreciation of great contemporaries.   Many incidents serve to show how much Napoleon thought of the distinguished scholar who had created a new department of science and attracted the attention of the world to his splendid work at Paris.   Not long after he became emperor, Napoleon named him Honorary Canon of the

Cathedral of Notre Dame; and when he founded the Legion of Honor, he made the Abbé one of the original members. Shortly after these dignities had been conferred upon him, it happened that the Abbé fell ill; and Napoleon, having sent his own physician to him, went personally to call on him in his humble quarters, saying to the physician: "Remember that you must cure Abbé Haüy, and restore him to us as one of the glories of our reign." After Napoleon's return from Elba, he told the Abbé that the latter's "Treatise on Crystallography " was one of the books that he had specially selected to take with him to Elba, to while away the leisure that he thought he would have for many years. Abbé Haüy's independence of spirit, and his unselfish devotion to his native country, may be best appreciated from the tradition that after the return from Elba, when there was a popular vote for the confirmation of Napoleon's second usurpation, the old scientist voted, No.

In spite of his constant labor at his investigations, his uniformly regular life enabled him to maintain his health, and he lived to the ripe age of over seventy-nine. Toward the end of his career, he did not obtain the recognition that his labors deserved. After the Restoration, he was not in favor with the new authorities in France, and he accordingly lost his position as professor at the University. The absolute simplicity of life that he had always maintained now stood him in good stead; and, notwithstanding the

smallness of his income, he did not have to make
any change in his ordinary routine. Unfortunately, an accidental fall in his room at the beginning of his eightieth year confined him to his
bed; and then his health began to fail very seriously. He died on the 3 June, 1822.

He had shown during his illness the same gentleness and humility, and even enthusiasm for
study whenever it was possible, that had always
characterized him. While he was confined to his
bed he divided his time between prayer, attention
to the new edition of his works which was about
to appear, and his interest for the future of those
students who had helped him in his investigations. Cuvier says of him that " he was as
faithful to his religious duties as he was in the
pursuit of his studies. The profoundest speculations with regard to weighty matters of science
had not kept him from the least important duty
which ecclesiastical regulations might require of
him." There is, perhaps, no life in all the history of science which shows so clearly how absolutely untrue is the declaration so often made,
that there is essential opposition between the intellectual disposition of the inquiring scientist
and those other mental qualities which are necessary to enable the Christian to bow humbly before the mysteries of religion, acknowledge all
that is beyond understanding in what has been
revealed, and observe faithfully all the duties that
flow from such belief.

VIII.

ABBOT MENDEL: A NEW OUT-LOOK IN HEREDITY.

THERE is grandeur in this view of life, with its several powers having been originally breathed by the Creator into a few forms or into one ; and that, while this planet has gone circling on according to the fixed law of gravity from so simple a beginning, endless forms, most beautiful and most wonderful, have been and are being evolved.—Closing sentence of DARWIN's *Origin of Species*.

GREGOR MENDEL

VIII.

ABBOT MENDEL[1]: A NEW OUTLOOK IN HEREDITY.

SCIENTIFIC progress does not run in cycles of centuries, and as a rule it bears no relationship to the conventional arrangement of years. As has been well said—for science a new century begins every second. There are interesting coincidences, however, of epoch-making discoveries in science corresponding with the beginning of definite eras in time that are at least impressive from a mnemonic standpoint, if from no other.

The very eve of the nineteenth century saw the first definite formulation of the theory of evolution. Lamarck, the distinguished French biologist, stated a theory of development in nature which, although it attracted very little attention

[1] The portrait of Abbot Mendel which precedes this sketch was kindly furnished by the Vicar of the Augustinian Monastery of Brünn. It represents him holding a fuchsia, his favorite flower, and was taken in 1867, just as he was completing the researches which were a generation later to make his name so famous. The portrait has for this reason a very special interest as a human document. We may add that the sketch of Abbot Mendel which appears here was read by the Very Rev. Klemens Janetschek, the Vicar of the Monastery, who suggested one slight change in it, so that it may be said to have had the revision of one who knew him and his environment very well.

for many years after its publication, has come in our day to be recognized as the most suggestive advance in biology in modern times.

As we begin the twentieth century, the most interesting question in biology is undoubtedly that of heredity. Just at the dawn of the century three distinguished scientists, working in different countries, rediscovered a law with regard to heredity which promises to be even more important for the science of biology in the twentieth century than was Lamarck's work for the nineteenth century. This law, which, it is thought, will do more to simplify the problems of heredity than all the observations and theories of nineteenth-century workers, and which has already done much more to point out the methods by which observation, and the lines along which experimentation shall be best directed so as to replace elaborate but untrustworthy scientific theorizing by definite knowledge, was discovered by a member of a small religious community in the little-known town of Brünn, in Austria, some thirty-five years before the beginning of the present century.

Considering how generally, in English-speaking countries at least, it is supposed that the training of a clergyman and particularly that of a religious unfits him for any such initiative in science, Father Mendel's discovery comes with all the more emphatic surprise. There is no doubt, however, in the minds of many of the most prominent present-day workers in biology that his discoveries are of a ground-breaking character that will furnish substantial foundation for a new development of scientific knowledge with regard to heredity.

Lest it should be thought that perhaps there is a tendency to make Father Mendel's discovery appear more important here than it really is, because of his station in life, it seems desirable to quote some recent authoritative expressions of opinion with regard to the value of his observations and the importance of the law he enunciated, as well as the principle which he considered to be the explanation of that law.

In the February number of "Harper's Monthly" for 1903, Professor Thomas Hunt Morgan, Professor of Biology at Bryn Mawr, and one of the best known of our American biologists, whose recent work on "Regeneration" has attracted favorable notice all over the world, calls attention to the revolutionary character of Mendel's discovery. He considers that recent demonstrations of the mathematical truth of Mendel's Law absolutely confirm Mendel's original observations, and the movement thus initiated, in Professor Morgan's eyes, gives the final *coup de grâce* to the theory of natural selection. "If," he says, "we reject Darwin's theory of natural selection as an explanation of evolution, we have at least a new and promising outlook in another direction and are in a position to answer the oft-heard but unscientific query of those who must cling to some dogma: if you reject Darwin, what better have you to offer?"

Professor Edmund B. Wilson, the Director of the Zoölogical Laboratory of Columbia University, called attention in "Science" (December 19, 1902) to the fact that studies in cytology, that is to say, observations on the formation, development, and maturation of cells, confirm Mendel's principles of inheritance and thus furnish another proof of the truth of these principles.

Two students working in Professor Wilson's laboratory have obtained definite evidence in favor of the cytological explanation of Mendel's principles, and have thus made an important step in the solution of one of the important fundamental mysteries of cell development in the very early life of organisms.

In a paper read before the American Academy of Arts and Sciences last year, Professor W. E. Castle, of Harvard University, said with regard to Mendel's Law of Heredity:—

What will doubtless rank as one of the greatest discoveries in the study of biology, and in the study of heredity, perhaps the greatest, was made by Gregor Mendel, an Austrian monk, in the garden of his cloister, some forty years ago. The discovery was announced in the proceedings of a fairly well-known scientific society, but seems to have attracted little attention, and to have been soon forgotten. The Darwinian theory then occupied the centre of the scientific stage, and Mendel's brilliant discovery was all but unnoticed for a third of a century. Meanwhile, the discussion aroused by Weissmann's germ plasm theory, in particular the idea of the non-inheritance of acquired characters, put the scientific public into a more receptive frame of mind. Mendel's law was rediscovered independently by three different botanists, engaged in the study of plant hybrids—de Vries, Correns, and Tschermak, in the year 1900. It remained, however, for a zoölogist, Bateson, two years later, to point out the full importance and the wide applicability of the law. Since then the Mendelian discoveries have attracted the attention of biologists generally.[1]

Professor Bateson, whose book on Mendel's "Principles of Heredity" is the best popular exposition in English of Mendel's work, says that an exact determination of the laws of heredity will probably produce more change in man's outlook upon the world and in his power over nature than any other advance in natural knowledge that can be clearly foreseen. No one has better opportunities of pursuing such work than horticulturists and stockbreeders. They are daily witnesses of the phenomena of heredity. Their success also depends largely on a knowledge of its laws, and obviously every increase in that knowledge is of direct and special importance to them.

After thus insisting on the theoretic and practical importance of the subject, Professor Bateson says:—

As regards the Mendelian principles which it is the chief aim of this introduction to present clearly before the reader, it may be said that by the application of

[1] This paper was originally published in part in the "Proceedings of the American Academy of Arts and Sciences," Vol. xxxviii, No. 18, January, 1903. It may be found complete in "Science" for September 25, 1903.

those principles we are enabled to reach and deal in a comprehensive manner with phenomena of a fundamental nature, lying at the very root of all conceptions not merely of the physiology of reproduction and heredity, but even of the essential nature of living organisms ; and I think that I use no extravagant words when, in introducing Mendel's work to the notice of the Royal Horticultural Society's Journal, I ventured to declare that his experiments are worthy to rank with those which laid the foundation of the atomic laws of chemistry.

Professor L. H. Bailey, who is the Director of the Horticultural Department at Cornell University and the editor of the authoritative " Encyclopædia of Horticulture," was one of the first of recent scientists to call attention to Mendel's work. It was, we believe, because of a reference to Mendel's papers by Bailey that Professor de Vries was put on the track of Mendel's discoveries and found that the Austrian monk had completely anticipated the work at which he was then engaged. In a recent issue of " The Independent," of New York, Professor Bailey said:—

The teaching of Mendel strikes at the root of two or three difficult and vital problems. It presents a new conception of the proximate mechanism of heredity. The hypothesis of heredity that it suggests will focus our attention along new lines, and will, I believe, arouse as much discussion as Weissmann's hypothesis, and it is probable that it will have a wider influence. Whether it expresses the actual means of heredity or not, it is yet much too early to say. But the hypothesis (which Father Mendel evolved in order to explain the reasons for his law as he saw them) is even a greater contribution to science than the so-called Mendel's Law as to the numerical results of hybridization. In the general discussion of evolution Mendel's work will be of the greatest value because it introduces a new point of view, challenges old ideas and opinions, gives us a new theory for discussion, emphasizes the great importance of actual experiments for the solution of many questions of evolution, and then forces the necessity for giving greater attention to the real characters and attributes of plants and animals than to the vague groups that we are in the habit of calling species.

It is very evident that a man of whose work so many authorities are agreed that it is the beginning of a new era in biology, and especially in that most interesting of all questions, heredity, must be worthy of close acquaintance. Hence the present sketch of his career and personality, as far as they are ascertainable, for his modesty, and the failure of the world to recognize his worth in his lifetime, have unfortunately deprived us of many details that would have been precious.

Gregor Johann Mendel was born 27 July, 1822, at Heinzendorf, not far from Odrau, in Austrian Silesia. He was the son of a well-to-do peasant farmer, who gave him every opportunity of getting a good education when he was young. He was educated at Olmutz, in Moravia, and after graduating from the college there, at the age of twenty-one, he entered as a novice the Augustinian Order, beginning his novitiate in 1843 in the Augustinian monastery Königenkloster, in Altbrünn. He was very successful in

his theological studies, and in 1846 he was ordained priest. He seems to have made a striking
success as a teacher, especially of natural history
and physics, in the higher Realschule in Brünn.
He attracted the attention of his superiors, who
were persuaded to give him additional opportunities for the study of the sciences, particularly
of biological science, for which he had a distinct
liking and special talents.

Accordingly, in 1851 he went to Vienna for
the purpose of doing post-graduate work in the
natural sciences at the university there. During
the two years he spent at this institution he
attracted attention by his serious application to
study, but apparently without having given any
special evidence of the talent for original observation that was in him. In 1853 he returned to
the monastery in Altbrünn, and at the beginning
of the school year became a teacher at the Realschule in Brünn. He remained in Brünn for the
rest of his life, dying at the comparatively early
age of sixty-two, in 1884. During the last sixteen years of his life he held the position of
abbot of the monastery, the duties of which prevented him from applying himself as he probably would have desired, to the further investigation of scientific questions.

The experiments on which his great discoveries
were founded were carried out in the garden of
of the monastery during the sixteen years from
1853 to 1868. How serious was his scientific devotion may be gathered from the fact that in

establishing the law which now bears his name, and which was founded on observations on peas, some 10,000 plants were carefully examined, their various peculiarities noted, their ancestry carefully traced, the seeds kept in definite order and entirely separate, so as to be used for the study of certain qualities in their descendants, and the whole scheme of experimentation planned with such detail that for the first time in the history of studies in heredity, no extraneous and inexplicable data were allowed to enter the problem.

Besides his work on plants, Mendel occupied himself with other observations of a scientific character on two subjects which were at that time attracting considerable attention. These were the state and condition of the ground-water —a subject which was thought to stand at the basis of hygienic principles at the time and which had occupied the attention of the distinguished Professor Pettenkofer and the Munich School of Hygiene for many years—and weather observations. At that time Pettenkofer, the most widely known of sanitary scientists, thought that he was able to show that the curve of frequency of typhoid fever in the different seasons of the year depended upon the closeness with which the ground-water came to the surface. Authorities in hygiene generally do not now accept this supposed law, for other factors have been found which are so much more important that, if the ground-water has any influence, it can be neglected. Mendel's observations in the matter were, however, in line with the scientific ideas of the time and undoubtedly must be considered of value.

The other subject in which Mendel interested himself was meteorology. He published in the journal of the Brünn Society of Naturalists a series of statistical observations with regard to the weather. Besides this he organized in connexion with the Realschule in Brünn a series of observation stations in different parts of the country around; and at the time when most scientists considered meteorological problems to be too complex for hopeful solution, Mendel seems to have realized that the questions involved depended rather on the collation of a sufficient number of observations and the deduction of definite laws from them than on any theoretic principles of a supposed science of the weather.

The man evidently had a genius for scientific observations. His personal character was of the highest. The fact that his fellow-monks selected him as abbot of the monastery shows the consideration in which he was held for tact and true religious feeling. There are many still alive in Brünn who remember him well and cannot say enough of his kindly disposition, the *fröliche Liebenswürdigkeit* (which means even more than our personal magnetism), that won for him respect and reverence from all. He is remembered, not only for his successful discoveries, and not alone by his friends and the fellow-members of the Naturalist Society, but by practically all his contemporaries in the town; and it is his lovable personal character that seems to have most impressed itself on them.

He was for a time the president of the Brünn Society of Naturalists, while also abbot of the monastery. This is, perhaps, a combination that would strike English-speaking people as rather curious, but seems to have been considered not out of the regular course of events in Austria.

Father Mendel's introduction to his paper on plant hybridization, which describes the result of the experiments made by him in deducing the law which he announces, is a model of simple straightforwardness. It breathes the spirit of the loftiest science in its clear-eyed vision of the nature of the problem he had to solve, the factors which make up the problem, and the experimental observations necessary to elucidate it. We reproduce the introductory remarks here from the translations made of them by the Royal Horticultural Society of England.[1] Father Mendel said at the beginning of his paper as read 8 February, 1865 :—

Experience of artificial fertilization such as is effected with ornamental plants in order to obtain new variations in color, has led to the experiments, the details of which

[1] The original paper was published in the "Verhandlungen des Naturforscher-Vereins," in Brünn, Abhandlungen, iv, that is, the proceedings of the year 1865, which were published in 1866. Copies of these transactions were exchanged with all the important scientific journals, especially those in connexion with important societies and universities throughout Europe, and the wonder is that this paper attracted so little attention.

I am about to discuss. The striking regularity with
which the same hybrid forms always reappeared whenever fertilization took place between the same species,
induced further experiments to be undertaken, the object
of which was to follow up the developments of the hybrid
in a number of successive generations of their progeny.

Those who survey the work that has been done in this
department up to the present time will arrive at the con-
viction that among all the numerous experiments made
not one has been carried out to such an extent and in
such a way as to make it possible to determine the number of different forms under which the offspring of hybrids appear, or to arrange these forms with certainty,
according to their separate generations, or to ascertain
definitely their statistical relations.

These three primary necessities for the solution of the problem of heredity—namely, first, the
number of different forms under which the offspring of hybrids appear; secondly, the arrangement of these forms, with definiteness and certainty, as regards their relations in the separate
generation; and thirdly, the statistical results of
the hybridization of the plants in successive generations, are the secret of the success of Mendel's
work, as has been very well said by Bateson, in
commenting on this paragraph in his work on
Mendel's " Principles of Heredity." This was
the first time that any one had ever realized exactly the nature of the problems presented in
their naked simplicity. " To see a problem well
is more than half to solve it," and this proved to
be the case with Mendel's straightforward vision
of the nature of the experiments required for advance in our knowledge of heredity.

While Mendel was beginning his experiments almost absolutely under the guidance of his own scientific spirit, and undertaking his series of observations in the monastery garden without any reference to other work in this line, he knew very well what distinguished botanists were doing in this line and was by no means presumptuously following a study of the deepest of nature's problems without knowing what others had accomplished in the matter in recent years. In the second paragraph of his introduction he quotes the men whose work in this science was attracting attention, and says that to this object numerous careful observers, such as Kölreuter, Gärtner, Herbert, Lecoq, Wichura and others, had devoted a part of their lives with inexhaustible perseverance.

To quote Mendel's own words :—

Gärtner, especially in his work, "Die Bastarderzeugung im Pflanzenreiche,"[1] has recorded very valuable observations; and quite recently Wichura published the results of some profound observations on the hybrids of the willow. That so far no generally applicable law governing the formation and development of hybrids has been successfully formulated can hardly be wondered at by anyone who is acquainted with the extent of the task and can appreciate the difficulties with which experiments of this class have to contend. A final decision can only be arrived at when we shall have before us the results of the changed detailed experiments made on plants belonging to the most diverse orders. It requires some

[1] The Production of Hybrids in the Vegetable Kingdom.

courage indeed to undertake a labor of such far-reaching extent ; it appears, however, to be the only right way by which we can finally reach the solution of a question the importance of which can not be overestimated in connexion with the history of the evolution of organic forms.

The paper now presented records the results of such a detailed experiment. This experiment was practically confined to a small plant group, and is now after eight years' pursuit concluded in all essentials. Whether the plan upon which the separate experiments were conducted and carried out was the best suited to attain the desired end is left to the friendly decision of the reader.

Mendel's discoveries with regard to peas and the influence of heredity on them, were founded on very simple, but very interesting, observations. He found that if peas of different colors were taken, that is to say, if, for instance, yellow-colored peas were crossed with green, the resulting pea seeds were, in the great majority of cases, of yellow color. If the yellow-colored peas obtained from such crossing were planted and allowed to be fertilized only by pollen from plants raised from similar seeds, the succeeding generation, however, did not give all yellow peas, but a definite number of yellow and a definite number of green. In other words, while there might have been expected a permanence of the yellow color, there was really a reversion in a number of the plants apparently to the type of the grandparent. Mendel tried the same experiment with seeds of different shape. Certain peas are rounded and certain others are wrinkled. When these were crossed, the next generation consisted of wrinkled peas, but the next succeeding generation presented a definite number of round peas besides the wrinkled ones, and so on as before. He next bred peas with regard to other single qualities, such as the color of the seed coat, the inflation or constriction of the pod, as to the coloring of the pod, as to the distribution of the flowers along the stem, as to the length of the stem, finding always, no matter what the quality tested, the laws of heredity he had formulated always held true.

What he thus discovered he formulated somewhat as follows: In the case of each of the crosses the hybrid character, that is, the quality of the resultant seed, resembles one of the parental forms so closely that the other escapes observation completely or cannot be detected with certainty. This quality thus impressed on the next generation, Mendel called the dominant quality. As, however, the reversion of a definite proportion of the peas in the third generation to that quality of the original parent which did not appear in the second generation was found to occur, thus showing that, though it cannot be detected, it is present, Mendel called it the recessive quality. He did not find transitional forms in any of his experiments, but constantly observed that when plants were bred with regard to two special qualities, one of those qualities became dominant in the resultant hybrid, and the other became recessive, that is, present though latent and ready to produce its effects upon a definite proportion of the succeeding generation.

Remembering, then, that Mendel means by hybrid the result of the crossing of two distinct species, his significant discovery has been stated thus: The hybrid, whatever its own character, produces ripe germ cells, which bear only the pure character of one parent or the other. Thus, when one parent has the character "A," in peas, for example, a green color, and the other the character " B," in peas once more a yellow color, the hybrid will have in cases of simple dominance the character "AB" or "BA," but with the second quality in either case not noticeable. Whatever the character of the hybrid may be, that is to say, to revert to the example of the peas, whether it be green or yellow, its germ cells when mature will bear either the character "A" (green), or the character "B" (yellow), but not both.

As Professor Castle says: " This perfectly simple principle is known as the law of segregation, or the law of the purity of the germ cells. It bids fair to prove as fundamental to a right understanding of the facts of heredity as is the law of definite proportions in chemistry. From it follow many important consequences."

To follow this acute observer's work still further—by letting the crossbreds fertilize themselves, Mendel raised a third generation. In this generation were individuals which showed the dominant character and also individuals which presented the recessive character. Such an observation had of course been made in a good many instances before.

But Mendel noted—and this is the essence of the new discovery in his observations—that in this third generation the numerical proportion of dominants to recessives is in the average of a series of cases approximately constant—being, in fact, as three to one. With almost absolute regularity this proportion was maintained in every case of crossing of pairs of characters, quite opposed to one another, in his pea plants. In the first generation, raised from his crossbreds, or, as he calls them, hybrids, there were seventy-five per cent dominants and twenty-five per cent recessives.

When these plants were again self-fertilized and the offspring of each plant separately sown, a new surprise awaited the observer. The progeny of the recessives remained pure recessive; and in any number of subsequent generations never produced the dominant type again, that is, never reverted to the original parent, whose qualities had failed to appear in the second generation. When the seeds obtained by self-fertilizing the plants with the dominant characteristics were sown, it was found by the test of progeny that the dominants were not all of like nature, but consisted of two classes—first, some which gave rise to pure dominants; and secondly, others which gave a mixed offspring, composed partly of recessives, partly of dominants. Once more, however, the ratio of heredity asserted itself and it was found that the average numerical proportions were constant—those with pure dominant offspring being to those with mixed offspring as one to two. Hence, it was seen that the seventy-five per cent of dominants are not really of identical constitution, but consist of twenty-five per cent which are pure dominants and fifty per cent which are really crossbreds, though like most of the crossbreds raised by crossing the two original varieties, they exhibit the dominant character only.

These fifty crossbreds have mixed offspring; these offspring again in their numerical proportion follow the same law, namely, three dominants to one recessive. The recessives are pure like those of the last generation, but the dominants can, by further self-fertilization and cultivation of the seeds produced, be again shown to be made up of pure dominant and crossbreds in the same proportion of one dominant to two crossbreds.

The process of breaking up into the parent forms is thus continued in each successive generation, the same numerical laws being followed so far as observation has gone. As Mendel's observations have now been confirmed by workers in many parts of the world, investigating many different kinds of plants, it would seem that this law which he discovered has a basis in the nature of things and is to furnish the foundation for a new and scientific theory of heredity, while at the same time affording scope for the collection of observations of the most valuable character with a definite purpose and without any theoretic bias.

The task of the practical breeder who seeks to establish or fix a new variety produced by cross-breeding in a case involving two variable characters is simply the isolation and propagation of that one in each sixteen of the second generation offspring which will be pure as regards the desired combination of characters. Mendel's discovery, by putting the breeder in possession of this information enables him to attack this problem systematically with confidence in the outcome, whereas hitherto his work, important and fascinating as it is, has consisted largely of groping for a treasure in the dark. The greater the number of separately variable characters involved in a cross, the greater will be the number of new combinations obtainable; the greater too will be the number of individuals which it will be necessary to raise in order to secure all the possible combinations; and the greater again will be the difficulty of isolating the pure, that is, the stable forms in such as are similar to them in appearance, but still hybrid in one or more characters.

The law of Mendel reduces to an exact science the art of breeding in the case most carefully studied by him, that of entire dominance. It gives to the breeder a new conception of "purity." No animal or plant is " pure," simply because it is descended from a long line of ancestors, possessing a desired combination of characters; but any animal or plant is pure if it produces *gametes* —that is, particles for conjugation of only one sort—even though its grandparents may among themselves have possessed opposite characters. The existence of purity can be established with certainty only by suitable breeding tests, especially by crossing with recessives; but it may be safely assumed for any animal or plant, descended from parents which were like each other and had been shown by breeding tests to be pure.

This naturally leads us to what some biologists have considered to be the most important part of his work—the theory which he elaborated to explain his results, the principle which he considers to be the basis of the laws he discovered. Mendel suggests as following logically from the results of his experiments and observations a certain theory of the constitution of germinal particles. He has put this important matter so clearly himself and with such little waste of words that it seems better to quote the translation of the passage as given by Professor Bateson,[1] than to attempt to explain it in other words. Mendel says:—

The results of the previously described experiments induced further experiments, the results of which appear fitted to afford some conclusions as regards the composition of the egg and pollen-cells of hybrids. An important matter for consideration is afforded in peas (*pisum*) by the circumstance that among the progeny of the hybrids constant forms appear, and that this occurs, too, in all combinations of the associated characters. So far as experience goes, we find it in every case confirmed that

[1] Bateson: "Mendel's Principles of Heredity." Cambridge: The University Press. 1902.

constant progeny can only be formed when the egg-
cells and the fertilizing pollen are of like character, so
that both are provided with the material for creating quite
similar individuals, as is the case with the normal fertilization of pure species.

We must therefore regard it as essential that exactly
similar factors are at work also in the production of the
constant forms in the hybrid plants. Since the various
constant forms are produced in one plant, or even in one
flower of a plant, the conclusion appears logical that in
the ovaries of the hybrids there are formed as many sorts
of egg-cells and in the anthers as many sorts of pollen-
cells as there are possible constant combination forms,
and that these egg and pollen-cells agree in their internal composition with those of the separate forms.

In point of fact, it is possible to demonstrate theoreti-
cally that this hypothesis would fully suffice to account
for the development of the hybrids in the separate generations, if we might at the same time assume that the
various kinds of egg and pollen-cells were formed in the
hybrids on the average in equal numbers.

Bateson says in a note on this passage that
this last and the preceding paragraph contain the
essence of the Mendelian principles of heredity.
Mendel himself, after stating this hypothesis,
gives the details of a series of experiments by
which he was able to decide that the theoretic
considerations suggested were founded in the
nature of plants and their germinal cells.

It will, of course, be interesting to realize what
the bearing of Mendel's discoveries is on the
question of the stability of species as well as on
the origin of species. Professor Morgan, in his

article on Darwinism in the "Light of Modern Criticism," already quoted, says the important fact (with regard to Mendel's Law) from the point of view of the theory of evolution is that " the new species have sprung fully armed from the old ones, like Minerva from the head of Jove." " From de Vries's results," he adds, " we understand better how it is that we do not see new forms arising, because they appear, as it were, fully equipped over night. Old species are not slowly changed into new ones, but a shaking up of the old organization takes place and the egg brings forth a new species. It is like the turning of the kaleidoscope, a slight shift and the new figure suddenly appears. It needs no great penetration to see that this point of view is entirely different from the conception of the formation of new species by accumulating individual variations, until they are carried so far that the new form may be called a new species."

With regard to this question of the transformation of one species into another, Mendel himself, in the concluding paragraphs of his article on hybridization, seems to agree with the expressions of Morgan. He quotes Gärtner's opinion with apparent approval: "Gärtner, by the results of these transformation experiments was led to oppose the opinion of those naturalists who dispute the stability of plant species and believe in a continuous evolution of vegetation. He perceives in the complete transformation of one species into another an indubitable proof that species are fixed within limits beyond which they cannot change." "Although this opinion," adds Mendel, " cannot be unconditionally accepted, we find, on the other hand, in Gärtner's experiments a noteworthy confirmation of that supposition regarding the variability of cultivated plants which has already been expressed." This expression of opinion is not very definite, and Bateson, in what Professor Wilson of Columbia calls his " recent admirable little book on Mendel's principles," adds the following note that may prove of service in elucidating Mendel's meaning, as few men have entered so fully into the understanding of Mendel's work as Bateson, who introduced him to the English-speaking scientific public. " The argument of this paragraph appears to be that though the general mutability of natural species might be doubtful, yet among cultivated plants the transference of characters may be accomplished and may occur by *integral steps* [italics ours], until one species is definitely 'transformed' into the other."

Needless to say, this is quite different from the gradual transformation of species that Darwinism or Lamarckism assumes to take place. One species becomes another *per saltum* in virtue of some special energy infused into it, some original tendency of its intrinsic nature, not because of gradual modification by forces outside of the organisms, nor because of the combination of influences they are subjected to from without and within, because of tendency to evolute plus environmental forces. This throws biology back to the permanency of species in themselves, though successive generations may be of different species, and does away with the idea of missing links, since there are no gradual connecting gradations.

A very interesting phase of Mendel's discoveries is concerned with the relative value of the egg-cell and the pollen-cell, as regards their effect upon future generations. It is an old and oft-discussed problem as to which of these germinal particles is the more important in its influence upon the transmission of parental qualities. Mendel's observations would seem to decide definitely that, in plants and, by implication, in animals, since the germinal process is biogenetically similar, the value of both germinal particles is exactly equal.

In a note, Mendel says:—

In pisum (i.e. in peas), it is beyond doubt that, for the formation of the new embryo, a perfect union of the elements of both fertilizing cells must take place. How could we otherwise explain that, among the offspring of the hybrids, both original types reappear in equal numbers, and with all their peculiarities? If the influence of the egg-cell upon the pollen-cell were only external, if it fulfilled the rôle of a nurse only, then the result of each artificial fertilization could be no other than that the developed hybrid should exactly resemble the pollen parent, or, at any rate, do so very closely. These experiments, so far, have in no wise been confirmed. An evident proof of the complete union of the contents of both cells is afforded by the experience gained on all

sides, that it is immaterial as regards the form of the
hybrid which of the original species is the seed cell, or
which the pollen parent !

This is the first actual demonstration of the
equivalent value of both germinal particles as regards their influence on transmission inheritance
in future generations.

It is only by simplifying the problem so that
all disturbing factors could be eliminated that
Mendel succeeded in making this demonstration.
Too many qualities have hitherto been considered
with consequent confusion as to the results obtained.

It is of the genius of the man that he should
have been able to succeed in seeing the problem
in simple terms while it is apparently so complex,
and thus obtain results that are as far-reaching
as the problem they solve is basic in its character.

Bateson, in his work, " Mendel's Principles of
Heredity," says :—

It may seem surprising that a work of such importance
should so long have failed to find recognition and to become current in the world of science. It is true that the
Journal in which it appeared is scarce, but this circumstance has seldom long delayed general recognition.
The cause is unquestionably to be found in that neglect of
the experimental study of the problem of species which
supervened on the general acceptance of the Darwinian
doctrine. The problem of species, as Kölreuter, Gärtner,
Naudin, Wichura, and the hybridists of the middle of the
nineteenth century conceived it, attracted thenceforth no
workers.

The question, it was imagined, had been answered and the debate ended. No one felt much interest in the matter. A host of other lines of work was suddenly opened up, and in 1865 the more original investigators naturally found these new methods of research more attractive than the tedious observations of hybridizers, whose inquiries were supposed, moreover, to have led to no definite results.

In 1868 appeared the first edition of Darwin's "Animals and Plants," marking the very zenith of these studies with regard to hybrids and the questions in heredity which they illustrate, and thenceforth the decline in the experimental investigation of evolution and the problem of species have been studied. With the rediscovery and confirmation of Mendel's work by de Vries, Correns and Tschermak in 1900 a new era begins. Had Mendel's work come into the hands of Darwin it is not too much to say that the history of the development of evolutionary philosophy would have been very different from that which we have witnessed.

That Mendel's work, appearing as it did at a moment when several naturalists of the first rank were still occupied with these problems, should have passed wholly unnoted, will always remain inexplicable, the more so as the Brünn society exchanged its publication with most of the great academies of Europe, including both the Royal and the Linnean societies of London.

The whole history of Mendel's work, its long period without effect upon scientific thought, its thoroughly simple yet satisfactory character, its basis in manifold observations of problems simplified to the last degree, and its present complete acceptance illustrate very well the chief defect of the last two generations of workers in biology.

There has been entirely too much theorizing, too much effort at observations for the purpose of bolstering up preconceived ideas—preaccepted dogmas of science that have proved false in the end—and too little straightforward observation and simple reporting of the facts without trying to have them fit into any theory prematurely, that is until their true place was found. This will be the criterion by which the latter half of nineteenth century biology will be judged; and because of failure here much of our supposed progress will have no effect on the current of biological progress, but will represent only an eddy in which there was no end of bustling movement manifest but no real advance.

As stated very clearly by Professor Morgan at the beginning of this paper, and Professor Bateson near the end, Darwin's doctrine of natural selection as the main factor in evolution and its practically universal premature acceptance by scientific workers in biology are undoubtedly responsible for this. The present generation may well be warned, then, not to surrender their judgment to taking theories, but to wait in patience for the facts in the case, working, not theorizing, while they wait.